GILBERT

DUCK FEET
(HEARTBREAK SOUP VOLUME TWO)
ISBN 1 85286 022 7

Published by Titan Books Ltd
58 St Giles High St London WC2H 8LH
First edition: May 1988
10 9 8 7 6 5 4 3 2 1

Published by arrangement
with Fantagraphics Books.
All text and contents copyright
© Gilbert Hernandez 1988
except introduction copyright
© Angela Carter 1988.
This edition copyright
© Titan Books Ltd 1988.
All rights reserved

Originally published in the US by
Fantagraphics Books   1800 Bridgegate St
Suite 101 Westlake Village CA91361

Designed by Rian Hughes

Printed and bound in Great Britain by
Richard Clays, Chichester, W Sussex

Duck Feet

A Heartbreak Soup

GRAPHIC NOVEL

RNANDEZ

TITAN BOOKS

CONTEN

GILBERT HERNANDEZ was born in Oxnard, near Hollywood, California, in 1957, and from an early age developed a love of films and comics. Although inspired by their vitality and scope, he did not consider a career in comics until his brothers, Mario and Jaime, encouraged him to join them in a self-publishing comics venture called *Love and Rockets*. A copy of this was sent to Gary Groth (the publisher of Fantagraphics Books and *The Comics Journal*, a critical magazine for the industry) who immediately offered to publish their magazine regularly. Since then, *Love and Rockets* has become increasingly popular on both sides of the Atlantic and has been translated into four languages. Initially, Gilbert drew the ambiguous fantasy character, *BEM*, but soon developed his cast of subtly defined inhabitants of his mythic town of Palomar, whose uniquely

interweaving adventures form the tapestry of *Heartbreak Soup*. Besides this continuing *meisterwerk*, Gilbert has also created other strips for *Love and Rockets* such as *Errata Stigmata*, *Twitch City* and *Music for Monsters*. His work has also been published in *Vortex* and *Anything Goes*, and he created the first four issues of *Mister X* with brothers Jaime and Mario (published during 1984 in Canada by Vortex Comics, and collected into a single edition by Titan Books). He cites his grandmother's tales of her childhood, and the work of Buñuel, Marcel Ophuls and Hector Babenco as the inspiration for his special brand of storytelling. He is currently developing another one shot graphic novel for Fantagraphics Books, and playing in a new wave rock band, Nature Boy, with his wife Carol and brother Jaime.

INTRODUCTION

Gilbert Hernandez' comic strips in the series *Heartbreak Soup* (of which this collection, *Duck Feet,* is the second portion available in Britain) are about gossip. Especially about yesterday's gossip, about the memories our parents share with us so we almost come to think that they are our memories too. The intimate folklore of family. Gilbert Hernandez' family, of course, is not my family, or your family, but this kind of folklore has a cross-cultural similarity, most of all in cultures where people often find themselves short of a bob.

Families, particularly extended families — and the families in *Heartbreak Soup* are often stretched to the limit — flourish best in small towns. This involves Gilbert Hernandez in a celebration of small-town life. In the very small town of Palomar (population 356), the narratives of its inhabitants' lives weave in and out of each other with the same claustrophobic compulsiveness of the lives in the marvellous novels of Louise Erdrich (*Love Medicine, The Beet Queen*), set in remote townships in the American mid-West.

The novel composed of interwoven small-town lives has a long tradition in the United States. Sherwood Anderson's *Winesburg, Ohio* (1919) is a classic. But Palomar is not in the United States; it is somewhere south of the border. And although the strip sometimes goes out of its way to pay homage to a painter, the great Mexican artist Frida Kahlo, there is nothing in the least 'literary' about *Heartbreak Soup.* Nevertheless, Hernandez shares the same project as Erdrich and Anderson: the recreation of a place and time that explains why and what we are, here and now.

Erdrich and Anderson were raised in communities much like the ones they write about. Gilbert Hernandez says that his stories originally came, mostly, from his mother, told 'with her apron on while she was making the dinner or ironing'. Stories about Mexico, when she was a girl, and her first years in the States. Gilbert and his brother Jaime, the *Love and Rockets* man, live in Oxnard, sixty miles outside Hollywood. In California, the signs in bus stations are in both English and Spanish; bilingual education is a burning public topic; the state is re-Hispanicising itself while you watch and yet its image and aspirations remain securely Anglo.

But the Spanish arrived in California first. Hence the place names: San Diego, La Jolla, Sacramento and so on. Indeed, they got to almost the entire bottom bit of the USA first: Arizona, New Mexico, Texas, Florida. After a century or so in the back seat, the Spanish are staging a come back, recolonising the lost territory of their empire; to such effect that I've seen towns like Palomar deep in the heart of Texas — towns just as fly-blown and dirt-poor, teeming with barefoot kids, in which English, if spoken at all, is a reluctantly acquired second language. This invasion has been caused by economic desperation, not a desire for cultural expansion; what will happen when the barefoot kids, children of recent immigrants, grow up and demand a share of the all-American apple pie is anybody's guess.

Oxnard, however, is suburban, multi-cultural, Los Angeles in miniature, with 'nothing to do at night', say the brothers. Neither Gilbert nor Jaime speaks more than the odd phrase of Spanish. Their position is complex. And Palomar is, for them, the Old Country; the foreign place where one's parents grew up; 'home' at second hand, the knowledge of which is our inheritance, not our birthright. It is a place known only to the children of immigrants, therefore one with a special resonance in the American imagination, and, increasingly, the British.

The daily life of Palomar is a cruel parody of the chaste suburbia pictured in that family newspaper strip of my childhood, *Blondie*. It is a world of brawling kids and feckless, licentious, drunken men, dominated in every sense of the word by endlessly fecund earth mothers and furiously sexy women. They might have come undulating straight out of the crudest kind of male fantasy if they didn't pack such big punches; such big punches that a man can boast of them, even regret their absence. A grieving widower laments: 'She needed no dishes to render me into submission, her flying dropkick was enough.'

Sexiest and most furious of all is Luba of the big breasts and uncertain temper. The strip charts her progress from humble beginnings, crammed with her kids in the van where she plied her original trade of bath-house keeper, to cinema proprietor with a nice house, with porch and fence, in a decent part of town. Not that any of this changes Luba: 'None of my daughters know who their fathers were... and I'm keeping it that way. They're too young to have to know what kind of men their mother was stupid enough to get involved with.'

These are matrifocal families in the main. Sisters, or female relatives — Luba lives with her cousin, Ofelia — share a selection of children. A foundling, like the irrepressible Carmen, will be fitted in somewhere. Paternity, as Luba notes, is hypothetical. And the men are often away, anyway, working or looking for work; employment opportunities are few in Palomar. Money is a problem.

After the routing of an incompetent male sheriff, law and order rest in the capable hands of one Chelo, former bath-house keeper, former midwife. Indeed, she brought most of Palomar's inhabitants into the world. Now, in the name of the law, she occasionally dispatches one of them from it. But, although Chelo has the power of life and death, and Luba is the eternal mother, the dominance of women in the community does not, it should be noted, prevent the men of Palomar from treating them like shit from time to time.

When is all this supposed to be taking place? Hard to say. Note that television has not yet come to Palomar. In the early days of the strip, nobody remarked on it. Nowadays, however, visitors congratulate the inhabitants on the absence of TV, and the inhabitants congratulate themselves.

But the absence of television, like the relative absence of cars, like the characteristic hour-glass shape of the women and the 'Silvana Mangano in *Bitter Rice*' type shorts they like to wear, like the flat-top haircuts of the men, are evidence that the town is stuck in the fifties even when its calendars tell you that the eighties are here. The roughest edges of poverty are absent too, edges as rough then as they are now. I don't think this has been done on purpose, as a cosmetic exercise; it has happened because Palomar is already suffused with the glow of second-generation nostalgia.

Enter the ghost of Gabriel García Márquez. Well, not ghost, exactly; he isn't dead yet. Shall we say, the vexed question of the influence on the Hernandez series of the Colombian author of *One Hundred Years of Solitude*, with its unique, remote, fantastic township of Macondo. *Heartbreak Soup* has been consistently compared with *One Hundred Years of Solitude* since the strips began to appear in the early nineteen eighties. Evidently Gilbert Hernandez didn't get around to reading the novel, although urged to do so, until a short while ago, but it soon made a personal guest appearance in the strip. Carmen and Heraclio, one of the few more-or-less happily married — indeed, one of the few more-or-less married — couples in Palomar come to blows over it. Carmen hates to see him reading. She throws *One Hundred Years of Solitude* away, screaming: 'This is the last time you're going to ignore me for this junk!'

Instead, Heraclio discusses the book with the more booksy Gloria; they engage in altogether too ostentatious a display of literary criticism for absolute seriousness, perhaps. There are things about *Heartbreak Soup* that makes me think Gilbert Hernandez must respond sympathetically to the politics of *One Hundred Years of Solitude*, but, of course, he didn't have to know about Macondo to invent Palomar. They are both places that existed once, in a continent caught between post-colonialism and neo-imperialism; but to think of *Heartbreak Soup* as a sort of Classic Comics version of García Márquez is to do Gilbert Hernandez a great disservice. What *Heartbreak Soup* is most like is life.

Both Hernandez brothers cite Federico Fellini's movies as a real influence, and it is easy to see why. Think of Fellini's own home town, with its top-heavy women, horny youths and venomous feuds, as he recreated it for his magical autobiographical film, *Amarcord*, a word that, in the dialect of Fellini's part of Italy, means 'memory'.

Heartbreak Soup is put together with such imagination and verve it is easy to talk about it as if it were a novel; and it isn't, of course. But it *is* fiction, a category that includes novels, movies, soap opera, sit com, tragedy, comedy and comic strips. Gilbert Hernandez is using the comic strip to tell us important stories about love and death and poverty and grinning-and-bearing-it and the past we all carry with us wherever we go.

Angela Carter,
January 1988.

OTHER TITLES BY THE HERNANDE BROTHERS

heartbreak Soup

ECCE HOMO

BETO SEPT 84

HERACLIO: AIR-AWK-LEO / TONANTZIN: TOE-NONT-ZEEŃ

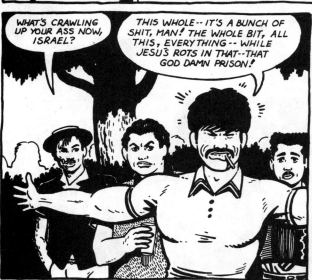

VICENTE: VEE-SEN-TEH/ISRAEL: EES-RYE-EL/JESÚS: HEH-SOOS/MARICELA: MARR-EE-SELL-AH

GUADALUPE: GWAH-DAH-LOO-PEH / DEMOÑA (DEMON GIRL): DE-MOE-NYUH / PIPO: PEE-POE / SERGIO: SAIR-HEE-O / GATO: GAH-TOE / MANUEL: MON-WELL

13

CHELO : CHELL-O

LIA: LOO-SEE'-AH / AUGUSTÍN: OW-GOOSE-TEEN' / BABOSAS (SLUGS): BAH-BOE-SAHS

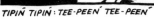
TIPIÑ TIPIÑ: TEE-PEEN´ TEE-PEEN´

16

HEH..I JUST NEVER NOTICED IT BEFORE...

IN HER YOUTH, OF COURSE.

WELL..! LONG AS SHE'S A GOOD ACTRESS...

...AND THEN HE SAID THAT SHE HOLDS A PLACE IN THE HEARTS OF ALL MEN WHO MAKE A PASS...OR SOMETHING LIKE THAT...

OH, TONANTZIN! TIPÍN TIPÍN SAYS THAT ABOUT ALL WOMEN! YOU KNOW THAT HE'S GOT NO TASTE!

I SWEAR, YOU BELIEVE EVERYTHING!

WELL, JUST THE SAME, I BET IF I WENT TO HOLLYWOOD, I COULD GET WORK THERE EASY, CARMEN.

YEAH, BUT I HEAR THEY'VE GOT ENOUGH WHORES AS IT IS.

BITCH--!

WHOOP--!

THAT...CARMEN'S PROBABLY RIGHT. SOMETIMES IT DOESN'T LOOK LIKE I'LL EVER GET OUT OF THIS...THIS TOWN. I'LL STILL BE HERE SELLING FRIED BABOSAS ON THE STREET TILL I'M AN OLD HAG. SNIFF...

...UNLESS I FIND SOME RICH GUY LIKE PIPO DID...

HEY, STRANGER! HOW'D YOU LIKE TO TAKE ME AWAY FROM ALL THIS?

EVER HAVE ONE OF THOSE GOOD DAYS.?

9

LOOKS LIKE YOUR SISTER'S LANDED A NEW BOYFRIEND, DIANA.

IF YOU'RE TALKING ABOUT TONANTZIN, YOU MEAN A NEW VICTIM.

NOW LISTEN HERE, BORRO! I'M HERE TO HAVE A GOOD TIME, SO I DON'T WANT TO HEAR THAT YOU'RE GETTING OUT OF LINE, OR I'LL--

RELAX, CHELO, RELAX. I USED TO BE SHERIFF OF THIS TOWN. I GOT A CLEAN-CUT IMAGE TO UPHOLD...

WELL, JUST DON'T YOU FORGET THAT I'M THE SHERIFF NOW!

CAN IT, YOU HOG. I'M HERE ON UNFINISHED BUSINESS...

--AND TODAY, BUSINESS IS A PLEASURE.

OH, CASIMIRA, GIVE ME A BREAK! YOU KNOW I'VE ALWAYS BEEN BAD AT THIS.

DA-- DA-- DA--!

HELLO, LUBA. AND YET ANOTHER OF YOUR CHILDREN AS BEAUTIFUL AS HER MOTHER...

OH... THANKS, BORRO. YOU LOOK AT LEAST HALF-HUMAN YOURSELF...

WHY HASN'T ANYBODY KILLED YOU TO PUT US OUT OF OUR MISERY?

HOW ABOUT IF I WHIP OFF YOUR TOP SO I CAN TITTY-FUCK YOU, COW?

TELL YOUR COUSIN OFELIA AND YOUR GIRLS HI FOR OL' BORRO, OK, LUBA?

WELL, I WOULDN'T HOLD MY BREATH...

BORRO: BOAR-O / CASIMIRA: CASS-EE-MEER-AH

18

IA: O-FELL-EE-AH

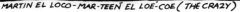

MARTIN EL LOCO-MAR-TEEN EL LOE-COE (THE CRAZY)

GET YOUR CLOTHES ON, TARZAN. I'VE GOT A SIXTEEN YEAR OLD SISTER LIVING HERE TOO, Y'KNOW.

WHERE... AM I..?

THIS IS MY HOME, REMEMBER? IN PALOMAR! YOU AND I MET AT A PARTY IN SAN FIDEO LAST NIGHT; OR SHOULD I SAY THREE HOURS AGO.

I REMEMBER. AND I ALSO RE MEMBER SOME THING ELSE...

NOT NOW, HANDSOME! YOU'RE GOING TO DRIVE US TO THE BEACH!

LET'S GO, DIANA!

SOME PEPPY CREW I'VE GOT. C'MON, THEO! TIME TO GET CRACKIN'!

Z!

AND SO IT'S OFF TO THE HARVEST WE GO--

... AND I HOPE YOU WIN THE TITLE BACK FROM BAD BOBO JONES, EL CLAVO.

CLAVO - SPIKE

AT HOME DIANA VILLASEÑOR IS ONLY TONANTZÍN'S LITTLE SISTER; AT SCHOOL, SHE IS AN AVERAGE STUDENT; BUT WHEN SHE RUNS..! WHEN SHE RUNS SHE IS ZEPHYRA, ONE WITH THE WIND...

WHILE DIANA BECOMES POSSESSED BY A GODDESS, TONANTZIN IS ACTUALLY NAMED AFTER GOD'S OWN MOTHER, THE PROTECTRESS OF THE EARTH, AND SHARES SOME SIMILARITIES WITH HER CELESTIAL NAMESAKE...

LEGEND HAS IT THAT CENTURIES AGO WHEN GOD THREW A TANTRUM AND FLOODED THE EARTH, TONANTZIN, IN AN ACT OF BOTH DEFIANCE AND COMPASSION, BREAST-FED THE SURVIVORS WITH PULQUE...

NOW, REMEMBER MY CHILDREN -- OH, JUST A SEC -- GOD! WILL YOU GET OFFA THERE?!

A FEW YEARS BACK OUR OWN T NANTZIN STAYED UP FOR FORTY-T HOURS STRAIGHT PREPARING DOZE OF BABOSAS FOR THE HOMELESS VICTIMS OF AN EARTHQUAKE THA STRUCK THEIR FAR AWAY VILLAGE

THEY'RE ALL YOURS, CARMEN!

OK, BOYS! LET'S LOAD 'EM UP! C'MON!

OUR TONANTZIN IS ONLY AS MORTAL AS ANYONE, OF COURSE; BUT THERE ARE THOSE FELLOWS WHOLLY CONVINCED THAT AFTER EXPERIENCING BOTH HER SPLENDID COOKING TALENTS AND SEXUAL PROWESS IN BED, SHE AND HER DIVINE NAMESAKE CAN ONLY BE ONE AND THE SAME...!

--THEN THERE'S ALWAYS THE FOLKS WHO PREFER LIKENING HER TO THE DEVIL.

PLEASE, TONANTZIN!! THE HEAD SCISSORS NEXT! THE HEAD SCISSORS NEXT--

KRRRUNCH!

BUT WE DIGRESS. BACK IN PALOMAR...

HERE YOU GO THEO. THE FRUI OF YOUR LABO

NO FRUIT! I WANT BABOSAS...

MAYBE I OUGHT TO STAY HERE TODAY HELPING YOU SELL THEM BOOGERS, HUH?

HO, YOU WISH! IF SHERIFF CHELO SAYS KIDS OVER SIX AND UNDER EIGHTEEN HAVE TO GO TO SCHOOL, THAT MEANS YOU, GIRLIE!

PULQUE - AN ALCOHOLIC DRINK HUMANS MAKE FROM THE MAGUEY PLANT

END

5

THE RETICENT HEART

BETO/8

ARRRRGH-- GET IT OFF-- GET IT OFF--

HERACLIO! HERACLIO, GET WHAT OFF?!

HERACLIO!

THE PANTHER--THE PANTHER-- THE WILD P--OH..OH, CARMEN..OH....

THAT NIGHTMARE AGAIN..!

OH, POOR BABY-- TSK.

HERACLIO, DARLING...YOU KEEP HAVING THAT DREAM OF A WILD ANIMAL ATTACKING YOU...

DID SOMETHING LIKE THAT HAPPEN TO YOU WHEN YOU WERE LITTLE? A CAT, OR...

UM, I. WELL, YEA I GUESS TH MUST BE I

ELL, I CAN'T TELL HER ABOUT BEING JUMPED Y THAT PANTHER THE TIME ME AND THE GUYS HAD GO LOOKING FOR JESUS IN THE MOUNTAINS A FEW MONTHS AGO. JEEZ..!

SHE'D COMPLETELY LIP OUT IF IT TOLD HER! HE'D--SHE'D--I DON'T WANT TO THINK ABOUT IT.

SHE THINKS I GOT THESE SCARS ON MY ECK AND SHOULDERS FROM FALLING INTO A BUSH.

HEARTBREAK SOUP VOL ONE, "THE LAUGHING SUN"-- BETO.

AT LEAST...THAT'S WHAT I HOPE SHE THINKS..!

HERACLIO, COME TO BED. YOU'VE GOT TO GO TO WORK-- OH. WRITING TO A SECRET ADMIRER?

I'M WRITING A LETTER TO JESÚS. HAVEN'T FOR A WHILE...

I DON'T SUPPOSE HE GETS A LOT OF MAIL BEING STUCK IN THAT PRISON. BUT I DIDN'T KNOW HE COULD READ...

OH, IT'S SATCH AND ISRAEL YOU'RE THINKING OF. JESUS AND VICENTE CAN GET BY OK, BUT SATCH AND ISRAEL; I DUNNO, THEY'RE STUBBORN...

AVRIL 1985

HERACLIO... AFTER WE WERE MARRIED...DID YOU HATE TEACHING ME TO READ..?

OH, CARMEN..! OF COURSE NOT. YOU WERE A WONDERFUL STUDENT. WHY?

BECAUSE I HATED EVERY SECOND OF IT.

DON'T STAY UP TOO LONG WITH THAT, OK?

2

CARMEN'S LESS THAN SUBTLE HONESTY IS SOMETHING HERACLIO HAS LEARNED TO ADMIRE IN HIS WIFE,

BUT···

FATE HAS SEEN FIT TO BURDEN HERACLIO WITH CERTAIN EXPERIENCES HE PREFERS TO REVEAL TO NO ONE, FOR FEAR OF HURTING THOSE HE LOVES.

FLASHBACK: A FEW YEARS BEFORE CARMEN AND HERACLIO BECAME WIFE AND HUSBAND ...

HEY KING DONG!

WELL, I WILL BE A SON OF A BITCH...

ALL RIGHT. WHERE'D YOU GUYS STEAL IT?

STEAL IT? HEY, MAN, I BOUGHT THIS BABY CASH MONEY!

NAW, REALLY. ISN'T THIS YOUR BOSS'S CAR, JESÚS? I REMEMBER YOU TELLING ME 'BOUT

HE LET ME USE IT OVERNIGHT. C'MON, ISRAEL. WE'RE GOING TO SAN FIDEO. BABES, MAN.

SHIT, I WISH. I'LL BE FINISHED HERE BY MIDNIGHT IF I'M LUCKY. LOOK AT YOU GUYS! DRINKIN' BEERS IN BROAD DAYLIGHT! WOTTA WORLD!

HEY SATCH, VICENTE SAYS YOU'LL PISS YOUR PANTS FIRST GIRL YOU MEET!

FUK YEH...

TSCH!

DOWNTOWN SAN FIDEO AT NIGHT--!

FOR THE JADED; SHIMMERING, SHALLOW PURGATORY...

AND THE RESTLESS YOUNG: AN OASIS AMID THE WASTE AND THEY FEEL THEIR LIVES...

34

EY, UH, LUBA'S RIDE TOOK F WITHOUT HER, SO IS IT OK SHE COMES HOME WITH US?

I DON'T TAKE UP TOO MUCH ROOM.

SURE.

NOW, IS LUBA AWARE OF THE FACT THAT JESUS HAS BEEN MORE THAN INFATUATED WITH HER EVER SINCE HE FIRST SET HIS BEADY PEEPERS UPON HER WOMANLY SPLENDOR..?

SO WHAT IS IT WITH GUYS, HUH? A GIRL JUST CAN'T DRESS UP NICE TO GO OUT AND HAVE A GOOD TIME DANCING AND DRINKING WITHOUT SOME JERK OR TWO SPOILING THINGS. I MEAN, JUST HOW MANY UGLY...NAMES DO MEN HAVE FOR WOMEN, ANYWAY? GRUNT...

I'LL NEVER FIND A MAN WHO WILL TRULY LOVE ME.

YOU'RE WRONG, WOMAN.

Y-YOU? BUT-- BUT I DIDN'T THINK YOU EVEN NOTICED ME.

MY HEART HAS ALWAYS BELONGED TO YOU...

HARUMF..!

OHHHH...I FEEL FAINT. HOLD ME...HOLD ME TIGHT. NEVER LET ME GO. I SHALL FOREVER BE YOUR SLAVE IN LOVE. YOUR WISH IS MY PLEASURE..!

6

...ESIDES, ISRAEL'S GONE TO ...ER FOR BATHS BEFORE AND ...E SAYS SHE DOESN'T. SAME ...ITH GABRIEL, LUTHER, THAT ...UY WITH THE SIDEBURNS...

HEY, JESUS. IF YOU'RE SO GOD DAMN CRAZY ABOUT THE BROAD...

HOW COME YOU'VE NEVER GONE TO GET A BATH FROM HER?

SATCH...SATCH, YOU DON'T KNOW NOTHIN'!

THERE WASN'T A SNOWBALLS CHANCE IN HELL HERA-CLIO MIGHT REVEAL TO HIS FRIENDS THE NATURE OF THE RE-COLLECTIONS RUNNING THROUGH HIS MIND JUST THEN. RE-COLLECTIONS THAT BEGAN THE MOMENT THEY PICKED UP LUBA FROM THE GAS STATION.

AH~!
BUT THERE'S NO REASON WHY **YOU** SHOULDN'T KNOW JUST WHAT THOSE RECOLLECTIONS ARE:
··· **FLASHBACK** WITHIN THE **FLASHBACK**···

YEARS AGO, ON A WARM, LATE AFTERNOON IN PALOMAR...

MOM WANTS ME TO QUIT MY JOB PASSING OUT FLYERS FOR SEÑORA LUBA'S BATHING BUSINESS...

BUT HOW AM I GONNA TELL THE SEÑORA WITHOUT GETTING MY BLOCK KNOCKED OFF? THAT SEÑORA GETS MAD PRETTY EASY...

...! I'M IN LUCK. HERE ...MES HER COUSIN OFELIA. ...L JUST TELL HER...

'SCUSE ME, SEÑORA, BUT ABOUT THIS JOB I HAVE WITH YOUR COUSIN...

TELL HER ABOUT IT! I CAN'T TALK TO HER WHEN SHE'S LIKE THIS!

COME ALONG, MARICELA.

ARGH... WELL, HERE GOES.

8

¡TOC TOC!

GET IN HERE.

SEÑORA LUBA? SEE, I, UH...

GOD, BUT THIS BATHING BUSINESS IS A GODDAMN PAIN IN THE ASS.

UH, Y'SEE, I CAN'T WORK FOR YOU POSTING FLYERS ANY MORE...

COME HERE.

I SCRUBBED AT LEAST THIRTY ME TODAY. NOW I' READY TO BE BATHED!

I...HAVE TO GO. M-MY MOTHER...

I PAID YOU IN ADVANCE TO DELIVER THOSE FLYERS.

WE CAN MAKE UP THE DIFFERENCE NOW.

...BETTER TAKE YOUR SHIRT OFF... WOULDN'T WANT YOUR MOTHER TO GET MAD.

WHAT HAPPENED NEXT, IN HERACLIO'S OWN WORDS :"...SEEMS LIKE A DREAM TO ME NOW. IT'S A MIRACLE THAT I DIDN'T WET MY PANTS. AS I SCRUBBED AWAY, LUBA LETHARGICALLY BEGAN COMPLAINING ABOUT H THERE WERE NO DECENT MEN IN PALOMAR, NO PHON HOW SHE WANTED TO OPEN A MOVIE THEATER 'CAUS NOBODY IN TOWN HAD EVER HEARD OF STERLING HAYDE

"I WAS SO DUMB AND CONFUSED AND SCARED I DIDN'T EVEN GET AROUSED...UNTIL SHE SET UP...OH, JEEZ--

"SHE THEN OPENED MY PANTS AND DOWN THEY SLI GENTLY SHE PUSHED ME DOWN ON THE SOFA AN WELL, IT DIDN'T LAST LONGER'N A FEW SECONDS, BUT SHE DIDN'T SEEM TO CARE EITHER WAY. SHE SMILED WHILE SHE HELPED ME ON WITH MY CLOTH

STAGGERED HOME WITH THE MIXED FEEL-
...S OF EXHILARATION AND CONFUSION
...T SETTING WELL IN MY BELLY. I LOVED
...E EXPERIENCE ...AND I HATED IT.

MUMMY!

IN THE MANY WEEKS THAT FOLLOWED, I DEVELOPED A REALLY
BIG CRUSH ON HER, NATURALLY, BUT SHE NEVER LET ME NEAR
HER AGAIN. I MEAN, WE SAID HI, BUT-- WELL, I EVENTUALLY
GOT OVER HER WHEN SCHOOL STARTED...

...AN YOU UNDERSTAND WHY I'VE NEVER TOLD ANY-
...NE? IT WOULD HAVE GOTTEN AROUND TO JESUS
...ENTUALLY FOR SURE! AND CARMEN! HAVING CAR-
...EN FIND OUT WOULD BE WORSE THAN FACING
...DOZEN ATTACKING PANTHERS! NO THANKS!"

...M GOING TO
...ARRY CARMEN
...MENEZ. SHE MUST
...VER KNOW ABOUT
...HAT NIGHT.

I'M NOT IN THE
HABIT OF RUINING
REPUTATIONS ...

ESPECIALLY
MY OWN!

NOW BACK TO OUR ORIGINAL FLASHBACK ...

SEE
YOU GUYS
LATER.

LATER,
BOYOS.

LATER.

LATER.

THANKS A LOT,
GUY. COME BY FOR
A BATH SOME-
TIME, HUH?

ALL
RIGHT.

SO WHEN'S THE
WEDDING, JESUS?

FUCK
YOU.

10

PRESENT TIME: MORNING COMES, AND IT'S OFF TO WORK FOR HERACLIO...

DON'T FORGET TO MAIL YOUR LETTER, SWEETHEART.

OK, QUERIDA.

G'MORNING, TONANTZIN. HI KIDS. HOW WAS TODAY'S HARVEST?

YOU'LL FIND OU COME DINNERTIM BOOGERFACE.

MORNING, SEÑORA.

GOOD MORNING, SEÑOR.

SAY, CHELO. EVER NOTICE HOW LUBA'S TEN YEAR OLD DAUGHTER LOOKS A LOT LIKE HERACLIO?

GUADALUPE? HM. MANUEL WAS HER FATHER. YOU REMEMBER; HE WAS KILLED...

MANUEL ..? OH, YEAH! THAT GUY WAS A REAL LOVERBOY--!

HERACLIO WAS ONLY WHAT, FIFTEEN YEARS OLD THEN? I SERIOUSLY DOUBT THAT HE AND LUBA-- YOU KNOW...

BUT WOULDN'T IT BE A SCREAM IF THEY HAD?

THAT STUFF ONLY HAPPENS IN LITTLE BOYS' HEADS, CHELO.

EN

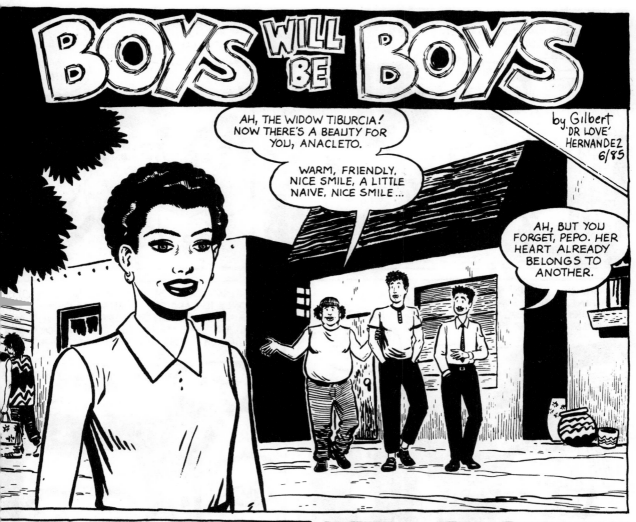

WELL, NAW. SHE'S GOOD LOOKING BUT WAY TOO STACKED. AND SHE'S GOT CHICKEN LEGS.

YOU LIKE LEGS? HOW ABOUT DIANA VILLASEÑOR?

OH, C'MON, PEPO! SHE'S JUST A KID! DON'T BE RIDICULOUS!

HEY! A WOMAN'S A WOMAN, HERACLIO! I'M TRYING TO SET UP MY LONELY PAL HERE!

HO--HO! WHO'S THAT?

SHERIFF CHELO? NOW, SHE'S A FINE, STRONG WOMAN INDEED! SHE PERSONALLY BATHES WHOEVER SHE ARRESTS BEFORE SHE LOCKS 'EM UP.

NO, NO. THE LITTLE ONE!

AH, NOW YOU'RE TALKING REAL BEAUTY, GUY! NOT ONLY IS CARMEN A PARAGON OF LOVELINESS, SHE IS ALSO A BRIGHT, PERCEPTIVE WIT, A FINE COOK, AND HAS MASTERED THE ART OF BODY MASSAGE...AND SHE USES-HER-WHOLE-BODY...

CARMEN...

IN MY MIND, NO FINER WOMAN EXISTS...

HEY, DID YOU SEE THAT? SHE WINKED AT ME! SHE--

AW, C'MON, HERACLIO! TELL HIM!

NO, HERACLIO! NOT ZOMBA! HE'S JUST A YOUNG MAN, HERACLIO! NOT ZOMBA..!!!

ZOMBA WOULD DESTROY YOU, ANACLETO. SHE'S TURNED THE STRONGEST MEN INTO QUIVERING HEAPS OF FLESH.

CRUSHED LIKE GNATS!

KREESH KREESH

MEN ARE BUT FOOD TO HER. SHE MUST DEVOUR A MAN IN ORDER TO LIVE...!

ZOMBA KNOWS A MAN'S WEAKNESSES, GUY, BE THEY INTELLECTUAL OR PHYSICAL! THERE ISN'T A MAN ALIVE WHO CAN RESIST HER MONSTROUS LOVE! PALOMAR'S FULL OF HER WRETCHED VICTIMS.

NO MAN IS SAFE WHILE ZOMBA WALK THE EARTH.

"SIGH"

SHE SOUNDS... TOO DANGEROUS.

BUT ISN'T THAT WHAT LIFE'S ALL ABOUT, ANACLETO?

SHE IS MISTRESS OF ALL SHE SURVEYS.

WELL, I APPRECIATE YOU GUYS TRYING TO FIND ME A GIRL AND ALL, BUT I OUGHT TO BE GETTING BACK TO FELIX NOW.

NICE MEETING YOU, HERACLIO.

OK, ANACLETO! SORRY WE COULDN'T BE OF MUCH HELP!

ANACLETO'S A NICE GUY, BUT NOT MANY OUT OF TOWN GUYS CAN HANDLE THE WOMEN HERE..

I DON'T KNOW MANY LOCAL GUYS WHO CAN EITHER.

SEE YOU LATER, PEPO.

GEE, ALL THAT TALK ABOUT WOMEN AND STUFF GOT ME PRETTY HORNY...

CARMEN'S NEVER IN THE MOOD THIS EARLY IN THE DAY, THOUGH..

WONDER IF SHE HAS STILL GOT THAT LINGERIE CATALOGUE LAYING AROUND...

47

AN AMERICAN IN PALOMAR

AS FAR AS HOLLYWOOD MOVIES GO, MY FAVORITES ARE THE OLD ONES; YOU KNOW, MOVIES WITH JIMMY CAGNEY, JEAN ARTHUR, MONTGOMERY CLIFT...

NOT TOO MANY PEOPLE SHOW UP FOR THE MOVIES I LIKE, BUT I'LL TELL YOU, THE PLACE IS ALWAYS PACKED FOR BRUCE LEE OR ELVIS PRESLEY. I THOUGHT THERE'D BE A RIOT WHEN I RAN 'VIVA LAS VEGAS'...

HEY, WOULD YOU KNOW WHY I CAN'T FIND ANY NEW BRUCE LEE MOVIES ANYMORE? HE SEEMED TOO YOUNG TO RETIRE.

BRUCE LEE DIED SEVERAL YEARS AGO. I DO NOT REMEMBER HOW IT HAPPENED, THOUGH.

OH.

HELL, I THINK WE'D BETTER KEEP THAT TO OURSELVES. IF ANYBODY AROUND HERE HEARS THAT-- WHOOSH!

HM. HE WAS SO CUTE, TOO, TSK...

SEÑORA, MAY I TAKE A FEW PICTURES OF YOU AND YOUR GIRLS HERE IN FRONT OF THE THEATER?

OH! WELL...!

I'LL TELL YOU WHAT. MY TWO OLDER GIRLS ARE IN SCHOOL RIGHT NOW, BUT TOMORROW'S SATURDAY...

WELL, HOW ABOUT TOMORROW AT NOON, WITH YOUR WHOLE FAMILY THEN?

UM... FINE.

THAT'LL GIVE ME TIME TO GET MY GIRLS ALL DRESSED UP NICE. NOT TO MENTION MYSELF. AH, NOW WE'LL HAVE A NICE PICTURE TO SEND TO RELATIVES.

HMMMMM ♪ ♫

'NICE' PICTURES ARE THE LAST THING HOWARD MILLER WANTS FROM HIS VISIT TO PALOMAR.

NO 'HOT' PHOTOJOURNALIST EVER GOT THE NOTORIETY MILLER SEEKS SHOOTING SUNSETS AND WATERFALLS.

...E MORE TRAGIC, HUMOROUS, ...NTIMENTAL OR WRETCHED ...E BETTER FOR MILLER, AS HE ...S FOUND IN THE PEOPLE OF ...LOMAR THE IDEAL SUBJECT ...TTER FOR THE BOOK HE HOPES ...LL ESTABLISH HIS (SELF-...ROCLAIMED) GENIUS TO THE ART ...ORLD...

WITH YEARS OF EXPERIENCE FREELANCING FOR VARIOUS GEOGRAPHIC MAGAZINES BEHIND HIM, HOWARD MILLER IS FAMILIAR WITH HIS CHOSEN SOURCE MATERIAL WHILE JADED BY IT AS WELL...

JUST ANOTHER GROUP OF INDIANS AND BLACKS AND WHATEVERS TO HIM...

HE BELIEVES IT IS HIS 'AESTHETIC GENIUS', HOWEVER, THAT WILL MAKE ALL THE DIFFERENCE.

AS FOR FRATERNIZING WITH THE NATIVES, MILLER HAS FOUND THEM TO BE QUAINTLY CONVIVIAL, IF SOME OF THEM PERHAPS TOO FRIENDLY...

MY GIRLS 'RE CLEAN, GUY. CLEAN GIRLS.

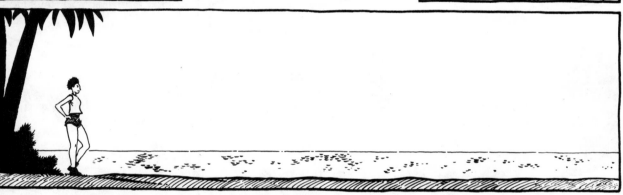

HO! HO! HO YOURSELF! HOW'D I DO? HUFF HUFF

10.94 FOR 100 METERS IS REALLY QUITE GOOD, DIANA!

⟨WISH I WAS SURE WHAT THE WORLD RECORD IS...⟩

LET ME DO IT AGAIN! ONCE MORE! ROWR!

AS OF THIS TIME, EVELYN ASHFORD HELD THE RECORD AT 10.76 FOR 100 METERS / 8-23-84

READY? SET? GO! GO! GO! GO! CLICK

YOW! ALMOST LOST MY HEAD FOR A SECOND--!! HUFF HUFF

9.98!

⟨HOLD ON! THAT CAN'T BE RIGHT! THAT'S WAY PASSED THE WORLD RECORD!⟩

DIANA! ONCE MORE! I WANT TO BE SURE!

10.97! STILL REMARKABLE! DIANA, IF THAT PREVIOUS TIME IS CORRECT... THEN YOU HAVE MOST LIKELY BEAT THE OUTDOORS WORLD RECORD FOR WOMEN EASILY!

I'M THE FASTEST GIRL IN THE WORLD!

NO YOU'RE NOT, DIANA, 'CAUSE YOUR SISTER TONANTZIN CAN CATCH YOU ANY OL' TIME!

REALLY? ⟨MY WATCH MUST BE WRONG. IT MUST BE--⟩

FOR YEARS HOWARD MILLER HAS ENTERTAINE[D] HIS OWN THEORY THAT THE *TRULY* GREAT ATHELETES OF THE WORLD NEVER ENTER OR NEVER MAKE IT TO THOSE SPORTING EVENTS DESIGNED TO DETERMINE WORLD RECORDS AN[D] SUCH...

MILLER CERTAINLY NEV[ER] EXPECTED TO HAVE HIS MUSINGS CONFIRMED I[N] PALOMAR..!

⟨AMERICAN ENGLISH⟩

--WHAT THE HELL DO YOU THINK WE ARE..? A FREAK SHOW--?

‹THAT'S -- THAT LUBA WOMAN'S VOICE..?›

SEÑORA LUBA? ARE YOU THERE? I AM AFRAID I AM A LITTLE LOST, HEH...

O YOU HAVE ANY NS OF TAKING ONANTZIN TH YOU...

‹WAIT--! NOW THAT'S ANOTHER WOMAN'S VOICE!›

GO BACK HOME AND WOMEN FUCKING GRINGO--

AND YET ANOTHER VOICE! PERHAPS A MAN'S..?

N-NOW WAIT A MINUTE--!

WHO IS THERE..?!

COME UT! SHOW OURSELF! HO IS THERE..?!?

-- LET'S GET DOWN TO BUSINESS--

¡STOP!

9

AN
AMERICA[
IN PALOM[

TO BE
CONCLUD[
IN PART
TWO

THE DAY BEFORE, THAT MAN FROM THE UNITED STATES TOLD HER SHE WAS POSSIBLY THE FASTEST WOMAN SPRINTER IN THE WORLD...

THIS IS THE REASON DIANA VILLASEÑOR IS UP SO EARLY ON A SATURDAY MORNING, A DAY WHEN HER OLDER SISTER TONANTZÍN USUALLY ALLOWS HER TO SLEEP IN.

UP UNTIL LAST NIGHT, THE ONLY ACTIVITY DIANA LOVED MORE THAN RUNNING WAS SLEEPING. THAT HAS NOW CHANGED.

THE FASTEST WOMAN IN THE WORLD.

THE PROSPECT OF THAT SENT DIANA'S IMAGINATION SOARING. SHE FANCIED THE ROAR OF CROWDS AS SHE WINS EVERY RACE, THE KISSES OF HANDSOME CHAMPION ATHLETES, AND OF BEING THE FIRST WOMAN ON MARS.

THEN, THE INEVITABLE LOW AFTER THE HIGH.

EXISTENTIAL CONTEMPLATION KEPT HER AWAKE MOST OF THE NIGHT, WHEN FINALLY SHE CAME TO A CONCLUSION:

DIANA HAS DECIDED NOW SHE MUST BE THE FASTEST OF ALL.

AN AMERICAN...

<Beth? It's Howard! What? Can't hear me? Wait, how's that? Yeah! I'm about ten minutes from a small town called Palomar!>

What's that guy saying? Sounds funny.

He's speaking English, I guess. I think he's from the states.

OASIS

<Yeah, well, my Spanish is holding up all right! I'll be staying in Palomar another day or so-- don't know which is worse here: the food or the music they punish themselves with! The beer's o.k., though. And there's no t.v.! Eh? Yeah, I'm renting a place where I've set up a little studio/lab! No rest for genius, y'know!>

Sounds more like Chinese to me!

<Finally going to get moving on that photo journal you've been threatening to start for the past two years, eh? OK, Howard. Where can I reach you?>

<What do you mean I can't?>

GEOGRAPHIC MONTHLY

<You can't! This is the only phone for miles! Hey, I'm talking a real secluded place! The last world news these folks got wind of was of the Dionne Quintuplets! Yeah, ha ha ...>

<OK, Beth, look, I'll try to get in touch with you soon as I can! Say hi to Bob for me! Right! Bye!>

COPYRIGHT ©GILBERT HERNANDEZ: 1985

<AMERICAN ENGLISH>

58

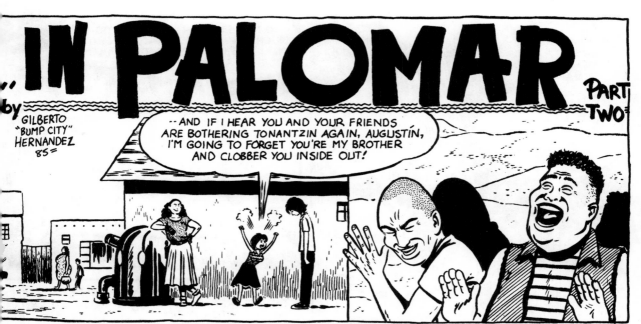

IT IS SO NICE THAT GOD HAS SEEN FIT TO GIVE YOU SUCH BEAUTIFUL CURLY HAIR, DORALIS, AND NOT THAT MATTED NIGHTMARE THAT GROWS FROM YOUR MOTHER'S HEAD.

HUH. THE POT CALLS THE KETTLE BLACK...

HOLD STILL, CASIMIRA.

MOM, IS IT TRUE WHITE PEOPLE COPY EVERYTHING THEY KNOW FROM NORMAL PEOPLE?

GUADALUPE! NO! WHO TOLD YOU THAT!?

NO, SWEETHEART, BUT THEY DANCE LIKE THEY'VE GOT WEBBED FEET, HUH, OFELIA?

DA!

LUBA, THAT'S ENOUGH!

YOUR MOTHER'S TALKING SILLY, GIRLS. SHE USED TO GO OUT WITH THIS ONE WHITE GUY YEARS AGO...

MMMMM, YEAH. BUT THAT GRIGORYEVICH ARTZYBASCHEV WAS A LIVING DOLL!

WHERE'S THIS WHITE MAN GOING TO TAKE OUR PICTURE AT, MOM?

OH, MARICELA, THAT'S RIGHT! HE WANTED US IN FRONT OF THE MOVIE HOUSE! TSK, I'LL TELL YOU GUYS WHAT--

YOU GIRLS FIX UP THE LIVING ROOM A LITTLE BIT, AND I'LL BRING HIM OVER HERE.

OK, LET'S GO, GUYS...

INDEED, A PORTRAIT OF LUBA AND HER FAMILY IS WHAT MILLER WANTS FOR HIS BOOK, BUT IT IS NOT QUITE THE PICTURE LUBA IS EXPECTING...

TOMORROW AT NOON, THEN?

FINE.

GREAT! HOPE THE REST OF HER FAMILY LOOKS AS BEAT!

5

MMMMM... GLAD TO SEE YOU'VE GOTTEN BACK TO SERIOUS BUSINESS, KID.

HOWARD AND I'VE BEEN BUSY BUSY BUSY, CARMEN. MODELING TAKES LONGER THAN YOU THINK, BUT HE'S A GENIUS SO IT WAS PRETTY EASY.

SO I HEAR. I ALSO HEARD SOME STUPID RUMOR THAT YOU WERE GONNA LEAVE WITH HIM TO THE STATES.

YEAH, SURE, I SAID, AND I SUPPOSE YOUR SISTER DIA GONNA STAY RIGHT HERE BY HERSELF, WHILE--

WELL, I'M TAK HER WIT US...

WHO KNOWS? MAYBE DIANA CAN GET A JOB AS AN ACTRESS OR SOMETHING HERSELF. I HEAR MOST FOLKS IN HOLLYWOOD SPEAK SPANISH ANYWAY, SO WE SHOULDN'T NEED HOWARD FOR TOO LONG; HE'S NICE, BUT, YOU KNOW...

NOW SCOOT, SHORTY. I'VE GOT TO FINISH HERE BEFORE DIANA GETS HOME. THIS BATCH OF BABOSAS MAY BE MY LAST.

TONANTZIN'S PROBABLY MY BEST FRIEND AND I LOVE HER, BUT SOMETIMES SHE GETS THE WRONG IDEA ABOUT THINGS...

SHE'S NEVER SHOVED ME OUT OF HER HOUSE BEFORE...

I'D BETTER TALK TO THIS GRINGO MYSELF...

NEVER CALLED ME SHORTY BEFORE, EITHER...

WHILE IT IS EVIDENT TONANTZIN KNOWS LITTLE OF THE WAYS OF THE WORLD OUTSIDE PALOMAR, PERHAPS LUBA KNOWS TOO MUCH...

SEÑOR MEELER.

<EGAD!>

SEÑOR MEELER, WE'VE DECIDED TO HAVE OUR PICTURE TAKEN AT OUR HOUSE. THIS OLD THEATER'S TOO UGLY, YOU KNOW...

OH...OH, BUT YOU MISUNDER-STAND, SEÑORITA. I WANTED YOUR FAMILY IN FRONT OF THE MOVIE THEATER BECAUSE...WELL, LET ME TRY TO EXPLAIN...

H OH. I'VE EN THAT LOOK LUBA'S FACE EFORE...

YEAH, HE'LL BE LUCKY IF HE WALKS AWAY WITH SIX TEETH LEFT IN HIS HEAD--

YOU WANT...A PICTURE OF MY FAMILY ALL SLOPPY AND RAGGED--TO PUT IN A BOOK FOR THE WHOLE WORLD TO SEE--?

WHAT THE HELL DO YOU THINK WE ARE? A FREAK SHOW--?

NO..! YOU DO NOT UNDERSTAND; I WANT TO SHOW THE BEAUTY OF YOUR TOWN... YOUR LIVES...

BEAUTY?! YOU'RE GOING TO MAKE HUNDREDS OF DOLLARS BY MAKING US LOOK BAD AND YOU'RE TALKING ABOUT BEAUTY?!

〈YOWCH!〉

THAT'S ENOUGH, GIRL!

KRAK!

¡·ⓖ★#*҂◎/¡*

〈¡ⓖ⚡*#!¡⚡〉

〈WHAT THE HELL DOES SHE KNOW ABOUT...ART!〉

〈EINSTEIN WARNED ME ABOUT DAYS LIKE THIS! HARUMPF--!〉

HEY, SEÑOR..!

⑦

<"GREAT SPIRITS HAVE ALWAYS ENCOUNTERED VIOLENT OPPOSITION FROM MEDIOCRE MINDS.">

<THAT'S WHAT EINSTEIN SAID, WOMAN! CHEW ON THAT A SPELL!>

HEY!

WAIT, WHAT..? SHE THINKS SHE IS COMING WITH ME--? WHATEVER GAVE HER THAT IDEA..?

OH, I CAN GUESS! NOW, IF YOU DON'T TALK TO HER SOON--

<DAMN! OF ALL THE GIRLS GET INVOLVED WITH, I WIND WITH A GODDAMN GROUPIE

WELL, IF I DON'T LOOK AFTER TONANTZIN, WHO WILL?

TONANTZIN! DON'T KEEP ME IN SUSPENSE! WHAT SURPRISE?! WHAT?!

DIANA, YOU'LL HAVE TO BE PATIENT. HOWARD WILL TELL YOU HIMSELF.

<CHRIST, THAT LUBA AND TONANTZIN GIVE NAIVETÉ A BAD NAME.>

<AH, BUT I SHOULDN'T BE ANGRY. I SUPPOSE BEING STUCK FOREVER IN A PLACE LIKE THIS WOULD IMPOVERISH ANYBODY'S LIFE. SAD...

<WELL, THE MOST BEAUTIFUL FLOWERS GROW FROM SHIT, SO MY BOOK WILL BE ONE GROUNDBREAKING BOUQUET. HEY. I MAY HAVE A TITLE THERE.>

<SIGH, TONANTZIN, TSK... WHAT WILL I TELL HER?>

<GUESS I SIMPLY TELL HER THE TRUTH: I'M COMMIT TO MY WORK; TO OTHER PEO. I'LL SIMPLY TELL HER...

LIES. LIES ABOUT HIS EDITOR SENDING HIM ON ~SIGNMENT TO RUSSIA FOR TWO YEARS AND OTHER ~NSENSE. HE DOESN'T KNOW WHEN HE WILL RETURN ~ THE STATES BUT ISN'T IT WONDERFUL?

THAT'S...THE SURPRISE YOU TWO HAD FOR ME?

SURPRISE... OH. OH! YES, DIANA, SURPRISE! MY STOPWATCH WAS CORRECT AFTER ALL.

~EALLY..? THEN... ~M THE FASTEST ~RL... OF ALL?

‹CHRIST. DID I REALLY SAY ALL THAT?›

WOW!

TONANTZÍN...

‹SHUT UP, MILLER. JUST DON'T MOVE OR SAY ANYTHING.›

9

YOU *SURE* YOU WANNA DO IT, AUGUSTIN? I MEAN, AFTER WHAT YOUR *SISTER* SAID...

SHUT THE FUCK UP. CARMEN DON'T TELL ME WHAT TO DO, ASSBITE.

HOLD IT! TARGET SIGHTED!

WHOOP WHOOP

SNIFF

!

HUH...

SNIFF

OH, TONANTZIN, STOP NOW...WHAT DID YOU EXPECT FROM A GRINGO?

HE-HE-HE USED ME... TOOK THOSE PICTURES OF ME...LED ME ON...HE USED ME...!

WHO USED WHO?! TONANTZI THOSE PICTURES WERE YOUR ID DID HE SAY HE WAS TAKING YO WITH HIM? JUST BECAUSE YOU SLEPT WITH HIM--!

CARMEN TAKE I EASY

JULIO
1985

66

...WINNER OF THE **KOVINICK PRIZE** FOR PHOTOJOURNALISM -- HOWARD MILLER!

THANK YOU-- THANK YOU

I WOULD LIKE TO THANK ABSOLUTELY NO ONE FROM PALOMAR FOR THIS PRESTIGIOUS AWARD, AS IT WAS ONLY THROUGH MY EXTRAORDINARY AESTHETIC EYE THAT FINE ART COULD BE CULLED FROM SUCH AN OTHERWISE DREARY, OVERUSED SUBJECT...

TO MY ARTISTIC PEERS MORE FASCINATED WITH MY SUBJECT, I SAY VISIT PALOMAR AT YOUR OWN RISK. I CAN'T GUARANTEE YOU'LL ALSO EXPERIENCE THERE THE KIND OF PHYSICAL AND EMOTIONAL PAIN THAT BEGETS ART, BUT THE FOOD AND MUSIC MAY BE ENOUGH FOR YOU...

-- AND BY NO MEANS FORGET OL' SEÑOR ALBERTO EINSTEIN'S GREAT QUOTE:

"GREAT SPIRITS HAVE ALWAYS ENCOUNTERED VIOLENT OPPOSITION FROM MEDIOCRE MINDS"..

--BECAUSE THE MEDIOCRE MIND YOU ENCOUNTER MAY BE YOUR OWN.

FWUD oo!

DESPITE THE LOOKS OF THINGS, TONANTZIN HATED TO DO WHAT SHE JUST DID, BUT FEELS SHE HAD NO OTHER CHOICE: IF SHE DOESN'T LOOK AFTER DIANA, WHO WILL?

C'MON. LET'S GET TO WORK.

OF COURSE, TONANTZIN'S LITTLE DISPLAY HAS ONLY SERVED TO ENCOURAGE DIANA EVEN MORE.

TONANTZIN SAYS THAT SHE DOESN'T MISS MEELER MUCH, SHE NEVER HAD ANY REAL FEEL FOR HIM. SHE JUST WISHES HAVE BEEN AROUND TO PAY HALF THE ABORTION FEE.

I'M HOPING HER ENCOUNTER WITH H HAS ONCE AND FOR ALL EXORCISE HER NAIVE ASPIRATIONS OF CONQUERING SHOWBIZ.

BUT WE SHALL SEE WHAT WE SHALL SEE.

AS TIME PASSES IN PALOMAR, THE DAILY RITUALS OF WORK AND PLAY EASE THE MEMORY OF HOWARD MILLER AND HIS PROPOSED BOOK OUT OF THE MINDS OF THE PEOPLE. MOST FOLKS HAVE ALREADY FORGOTTEN HIS NAME, MUCH LESS REMEMBER HIS FACE.

BACK IN THE UNITED STATES MILLER WISHES HE COULD BE SO LUCKY.

holidays in the Sun

74

TWITCH CITY

HEY THERE, BOY. I THINK YOU'D BETTER HAVE A LOOK AT THIS...

WHEN..WHEN I GET OUTTA HERE ≥HOFF HOFF≥ I'M GONNA MARRY YOU-- ≥HOFF HOFF≥ I MEAN IT ≥ HOFF≥...

BUT, JESUS... WE ARE ALREADY MARRIED...

JESUS HAS NEVER TOUCHED LUBA IN REALITY, BUT HAS HAD OVER FIFTEEN THOUSAND DIFFERENT FANTASIES OF THE WOMAN FROM THE MOMENT HE FIRST SET EYES ON HER SOME TWELVE YEARS AGO IN PALOMAR...

NOW, TO JESUS'S CONFUSION, HIS ESTRANGED WIFE LAURA IS REPLACING LUBA MIDWAY THROUGH THESE IMAGINARY INTERLUDES.

BUT WHY? LAURA IS THE LAST PERSON HE WANTS TO THINK ABOUT...

I'M TELLING YOU, JESUS, THAT DROMUNDO DOESN'T SCARE ME ONE BIT!

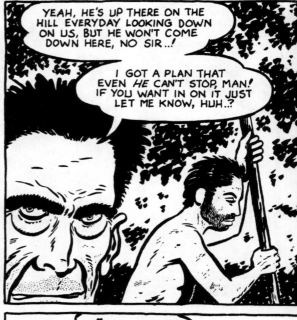

YEAH, HE'S UP THERE ON THE HILL EVERYDAY LOOKING DOWN ON US, BUT HE WON'T COME DOWN HERE, NO SIR...!

I GOT A PLAN THAT EVEN HE CAN'T STOP, MAN! IF YOU WANT IN ON IT JUST LET ME KNOW, HUH..?

♪ JESUS... ♪

THE HELL WITH THAT NOISE, BOY! C'MON IN! THE WATER'S FINE!

NO. NOT LUBA. SOMEONE ELSE. THINK OF SOMEONE ELSE. LUBA ONLY LEADS TO LAURA.

♪ JESUS ♪

AH, TONANTZIN! THERE YOU GO. SHE AND JESUS HAD QUITE AN AFFAIR GOING A YEAR OR SO BEFORE HE WAS SENT HERE. LOVELY, VIVIFYING, SERENE TONANTZIN...

SUCCESS. LAURA IS NOWHERE TO BE FOUND IN HIS FANTASIES OF TONANTZIN... BUT IT IS TOO LATE: TRYING NOT TO THINK OF SOMETHING USUALLY LEADS TO THINKING ABOUT IT...

7

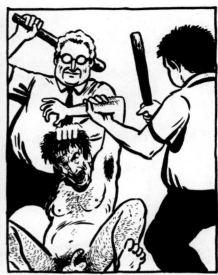

LOVE?! YOU ONLY LIKED ME PREGNANT BECAUSE IT *TURNED YOU ON!* LOVE. YOU ONLY LOVE SOMETHING IF IT GIVES YOU A HARD ON! DID YOU *'LOVE'* ME AFTER THE BABY WAS BORN? DON'T THINK I DON'T KNOW ABOUT YOU AND THAT *SLUT* TONANTZIN··!

IT'S TRUE; I WASN'T MUCH HELP. I DIDN'T LOVE YOU EITHER. WE'RE EVEN. YOUR TANTRUM WAS THE BEST THING THAT EVER HAPPENED TO US.

WHEN YOU GET OUT YOU WON'T HAVE TO SEE ME EVER AGAIN.

BUT···THE BABY··OUR BABY··

SHINK SHINK SHINK SHINK SHINK

HEY··· HEY, OBREGON. YO WERE GONNA T ME SOMETHIN ABOUT A PLA

82

13

IT'S ABOUT US, CARMEN. IT'S ABOUT OUR LIVES, UH...WELL, NOT *OUR* LIVES, BUT-- OK, THIS:

REBECA BUENDÍA GOT UP AT THREE IN THE MORNING WHEN SHE LEARNED THAT AURELIANO WOULD BE SHOT.

SHE STAYED IN THE BEDROOM IN THE DARK, WATCHING THE CEMETERY WALL THROUGH THE HALF-OPENED WINDOW AS THE BED ON WHICH SHE SAT SHOOK WITH JOSE ARCADIO'S SNORING.

IF YOU SAY SO, SWEETHEART.

OK, CLASS. THAT'LL BE IT FOR TODAY.

PRACTICE THOSE CHORDS, YSLAS.

HEY, PROFESOR! EVEN A MUSIC TEACHER NEEDS A DRINK NOW AND THEN!

OH, GLORIA, THANKS, BUT I DON'T WANT TO MISS THE BUS...

I'LL DRIVE YOU HOME, SILLY. HERACLIO, IF YOU DON'T LOOSEN UP YOU'RE GOING TO WIND UP LOOKING LIKE THAT *MUNCH* PRINT.

THAT BAD, HUH? *HEH*, MY WIFE MADE ME TAKE IT OUT OF THE HOUSE BECAUSE A GUEST MIGHT THINK THEIR HOSTS HAD PAINT-ED SUCH A THING.

ACTUALLY, *I'M* THE ONE WHO SOMETIMES FEELS THAT WAY WH I'M TEACHING MY GRAMMAR CL

WHAT'S THE POINT?

WHO EVER *REALLY* LEARN ANYTHING

EEAAAUUURR

HIDALGO ALONSO QUIJANA-- WAIT, DON'T [TE]LL ME... HIDALGO ALONSO [QU]IJANA IS IN FACT DON [Q]UIXOTE HIMSELF BY CERVANTES!

AH, ALMOST HAD YOU THERE, HERACLIO! OOH, NOW *THERE'S* A SIGHT! I SURE ENVY YOU YOUR EXOTIC NEIGHBORHOOD. I'VE GOT THE MOST INSPIRING VIEW OF THE PICKLE FACTORY FROM MY PLACE.

[O]H..UH, OK: [W]HO IS [QUE]EQUEG?

OH, YOU'LL HAVE TO DO BETTER THAN THAT. HE'S ISHMAEL'S CANNIBAL FRIEND IN *MOBY DICK* BY HERMAN MELVILLE.

HOW ABOUT RASKOLNIKOV?

RASKOLNIKOV..? OH, GOOD OL' RASKOLNIKOV! HE, UH... HE'S FROM *WAR AND PEACE.* SHE..?

NOPE.

NOT *WAR AND PEACE!* I MEANT *THE BROTHERS KARAMAZOV! LOLITA?*

AH, PALOMAR. THE BEAUTIFUL SIGHT OF NO T.V. ANTENNAS. YOU PEOPLE MUST HAVE ALL THE TIME IN THE WORLD TO READ. CAN I RECOMMEND *CRIME AND PUNISHMENT* BY FYODOR DOSTOYEVSKY? A RARE EXPERIENCE INDEED.

MMMM. WELL, HERE'S ONE YOU'LL NEVER GET: WHO'S *PRUDENCIO AGUILAR?*

PRUDENCIO AGUILAR.. PRUDENCIO.. HMM... WELL, SEÑOR, YOU GOT ME WITH THAT ONE.

HA!

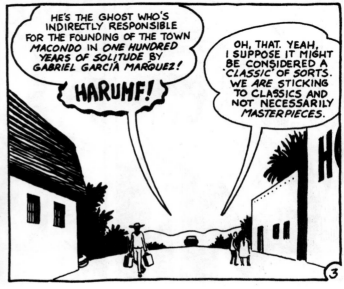

HE'S THE GHOST WHO'S INDIRECTLY RESPONSIBLE FOR THE FOUNDING OF THE TOWN MACONDO IN *ONE HUNDRED YEARS OF SOLITUDE* BY GABRIEL GARCÍA MARQUEZ!

HARUMF!

OH, THAT. YEAH, I SUPPOSE IT MIGHT BE CONSIDERED A 'CLASSIC' OF SORTS. WE *ARE* STICKING TO CLASSICS AND NOT NECESSARILY *MASTERPIECES.*

③

87

WHA--WHAT DO YOU MEAN? 'COURSE IT'S A MASTERPIECE! IT'S FLAWLESS!

SURE, IF YOU LIKE RELENTLESS REPETITION AND CHILDISH HYPERBOLE. ACTUALLY, I DID FIND SCATTERED BITS OF IT TO BE QUITE NICE...

NICE--?! IT'S FUNNY AND SAD AND WARM AND SLEAZY AND--- AND PROGRESSIVE AND CRAZY AND INTELLIGENT AND JUST PLAIN BRILLIANT--!

HM. YOU MUS MEAN THAT TI I WAS TALKI ABOUT...

WELL, GLORIA, I REALLY APPRECIATE THE RIDE EVEN THOUGH YOUR CYNICISM BETRAYS YOUR ABILITY TO COMPREHEND TRUE BRILLIANCE.

WELL, HERACLIO, THE PLEASURE IS ALL MINE EVEN THOUGH YOUR POWERS OF DISCRIMINATION ARE IMPOVERISHED DUE TO AN ARRESTED ADOLESCENCE. SEE YOU MONDAY.

THAT GLORIA. SHE'S A DOLL.

WHY ARE ALL THE GOOD ONES EITHER GAY OR MARRIED..!

HO HO! YOUR SECRET'S SAFE WITH US, BUDDYBOY! SHE'S PRIME CUT!

FORGET IT, GUYS. CARMEN KNOWS THAT GLORIA'S JUST A FRIEND.

WITH FRIENDS LIKE THAT, WHO NEEDS A WIFE?

HYAK!

IT'S A MAN'S WORLD, HERACLIO! YOU HAVE A RIGHT TO ALL THE PUSSY YOU WANT, BOY!

OH, GREAT, GUYS! NOW I'LL NEVER GET ANY SLEEP.

TIVOLI NIGHTS

NOW *WHY* DID I DO THAT? CARMEN DISLIKES LUBA ENOUGH AS IT IS.

OK, CARMEN. I'LL SEE YOU TOMORROW.

IS IT...UH, SAFE TO GO IN, TONANTZIN?

SEE FOR YOURSELF.

YOU BETTER EAT BEFORE THE SOUP GETS COLD.

MMHMMM..

TILL THE DAY HE DIES HERACLIO WILL NOT REMEMBER EXACTLY WHAT IT WAS THAT HE WHISPERED LOVINGLY INTO HIS WIFE'S EAR...

SWO

HOW **DARE** YOU STICK UP FOR THAT **COW** IN FRONT OF MY BEST FRIEND, **EMBARRASSING ME--!**

OUT! GO EAT DINNER WITH YOUR **GODDAMN BOOKS!!!**

SEE HERE NOW...

IS HE HURT?

NO, YOU GO TO BED. I'LL TAKE CARE OF THIS.

WHAT A PAL WHAT A PAL WHAT A PAL..

AND WITH PALS LIKE YOU, WHO NEEDS A WIFE, EH..?

MUA!

YOU WOULDN'T CLOBBER ME WITH A BOWL OF HOT SOUP, WOULD YOU PAL!?!

NO, BUT THE MERE THOUGHT MAKES MY MOUTH WATER ...

GOOD OL' LUBA...YOU'VE PROBABLY TAKEN MORE SHIT THAN ANYBODY IN THIS GODDAMN TOWN OF NEANDERTHALS! GUYS ALWAYS BUGGING YOU AND SHIT, WOMEN WITH THEIR DAMN GOSSIP..

YOU'VE GOT MORE GUTS AND TOLERANCE OF ANYONE I KNOW, LUBA. WHY DO YOU STAY IN PALOMAR? WHAT'S IN IT FOR YOU..?

MMHMM...

H, I'M HERE BECAUSE OF MY E CARMEN...SHE LOVES THIS TOWN, PEOPLE..WELL, NOT EVERYBODY. SHE'S TOO CRAZY ABOUT YOU, Y'KNOW...

A FRIEND TRIED TO TELL ME THAT WAS ECAUSE CARMEN AND I HAVEN'T BEEN ABLE TO HAVE KIDS AND YOU'RE NOT MARRIED AND YOU'VE GOT FOUR GIRLS RUNNING AROUND. I DUNNO, CARMEN WON'T SAY ANYTHING...

V, CAN SHE BE UNREASONABLE! HE KNEW ABOUT THAT T YEARS AGO EN YOU AND ME-- Z ...

LUBA HAD ALMOST FORGOTTEN ABOUT THAT ENCOUNTER. IT WAS SUCH A TRIVIAL MATTER TO HER THEN THAT SHE WAS NOT CERTAIN WHICH OF THE BOYS SHE HAD SEDUCED THAT NIGHT...

HEY, LUBA...ABOUT THAT NIGHT..? WHY... HOW COME? I MEAN, I WAS JUST A DUMB KID, I DIDN'T... WHY? WHAT WAS IN IT FOR YOU..?

9

"UR-URSULA..SAW...PRU-DEN-CIO..AG-UI--AGUILAR..AGAIN...IN..THE..BATHROOM...UM, US-ING...THE..ES-ES-PAR-TO..PLUG..TO..WASH THE..CLOT-TED..BLOOD..FROM...HIS..TH-TH--"

WHO'S THERE..? CARMEN? WHAT'S WRONG?

OH. OK, C'MON IN.

THE WAY THINGS'RE GOING

VICENTE CAME HOME ONE DAY LOOKING PRETTY BEAT. HE HAD JUST LOST HIS JOB AT THE PLANT.

HE SAID THEY DIDN'T GIVE HIM ANY REASON FOR THE SACK AND WHEN HE WENT TO TALK TO ONE OF THE BOSSES, GATO, A GUY HE'S KNOWN FOR AT LEAST TWENTY YEARS, THE BUM SAYS "IT'S OUT OF MY HANDS." AND THAT WAS IT! LIKE KNOWING A GUY FOR TWENTY YEARS DOESN'T MEAN A GODDAMN THING! THEY WEREN'T BOSOM BUDDIES BUT THEY WEREN'T GODDAMN ENEMIES, EITHER!

I'D BEEN OUT OF A JOB MYSELF THREE WEEKS WITH NO PROSP IN SIGHT. I WAS ALREADY DOWN MY LAST FEW BUCKS AND MOST VICENTE'S LAST CHECK WENT TO PAYING OFF HIS DEBTS. DON'T E MENTION WOMEN...

I FORGET WHY, BUT WE GOT INTO A FIST FIGHT. I BUST TWO KNUCKLES 'CAUSE THAT RIGHT SIDE OF HIS FACE IS PRETTY TOUGH. HE WALKS OUT WITH ONLY A POPPED LIP.

VICENTE COMES BACK WITH A BOTTLE OF CHEAP WIN AND WE'RE PALS AGAIN.

PUT ON OUR GOOD SUITS AND HIT DOWNTOWN. INSTEAD OF JOBS [FAL]LING INTO OUR LAPS, WE FIND OURSELVES IN THE MIDST OF [DO]ZENS OF PEOPLES IN THEIR GOOD SUITS WITH THE SAME LOOK [ON] THEIR FACES THAT I'VE BEEN SEEING IN THE MIRROR LATELY.

WE MUST HAVE COVERED THIRTY PLACES THAT DAY. EVERYWHERE WE WENT THERE MUST HAVE BEEN AT LEAST TWENTY GUYS AHEAD OF US. CONSTRUCTION JOBS, CARWASHES, DISHWASHERS, EVEN THE LOWEST SHIT JOBS WERE TAKEN; THE JOBS ONLY THE POOREST OF THE POOR LOCAL INDIANS USUALLY ACCEPT. VICENTE AND I CONSIDER BECOMING HOUSEWIVES.

[LA]TER WE MEET UP WITH A FRIEND OF VICENTE'S FROM PALOMAR [NA]MED LUBA. I DON'T USUALLY GET ALONG WITH THEM INDIANS [FRO]M UP NORTH, BUT SHE'S O.K; SHE'S NOT STUCK UP LIKE [RE]ST OF HER PEOPLE.

WHILE THEY SHOOT THE SHIT I STEP OVER TO THE CURB TO SCRAPE OFF SOME DRIED DOGSHIT FROM MY HEEL. THIS LADY PASSING BY LOOKS AT VICENTE AND LUBA AND CRACKS TO HER FRIEND, "NOW AREN'T THEY A PAIR..."

[VIC]ENTE AND LUBA OVERHEAR THIS AND [THE]Y FIGURE THE BITCH WAS REFERRING [TO] VICENTE'S MISMATCHED SHOES. HE [WA]S HOPING NO ONE'D NOTICE THAT HE [HA]D DYED A BROWN RIGHT SHOE TO [MA]TCH HIS BLACK LEFT ONE.

AFTER LUBA'S GONE VICENTE TELLS ME HE DIDN'T MENTION TO HER OUR SORRY SITUATION EVEN THOUGH HE WAS SURE SHE WOULD'VE BEEN GLAD TO HELP US OUT MONEYWISE. PRIDE. IT'LL KILL YOU, I'M TELLING YOU.

THAT NIGHT AT HOME I MAKE MY USUAL SOUNDS ABOUT JOINING THE ARMY AND ONCE AGAIN VICENTE TALKS ME OUT OF IT...

②

VICENTE FIGURES WE'LL BE FIGHTING THE U.S. FOR SOME REASON OR ANOTHER SOONER OR LATER. HE'S PROBABLY RIGHT, THE WAY THINGS ARE GOING...

AS I DRIFTED OFF TO SLEEP I RECALLED SOME PARTICULAR NEWS FRO[M] THE U.S. I'D HEARD THAT DAY: A MARRIED MAN AND WOMAN WERE ATTACKED ON THE STREET BY TEENAGED BOYS WHO MISTOOK THE WOM[AN] FOR A GUY. UH...DID THOSE GUYS EXPECT TO KILL THAT COUPLE, BECA[USE] THEY DIDN'T; OR DID THEY THINK A BLACK EYE OR A BUSTED ARM WILL PREVENT THE SPREAD OF A.I.D.S..?

YEAH, WELL, THE WAY THING[S] ARE GOING THE EARTH OUG[HT] TO BE ASSUMED FLAT AGAIN [IN] A FEW YEARS...

I HAVE THIS DREAM AND VICENTE'S FRIEND LUBA'S IN IT. SHE'S FALLEN INTO THIS DEEP HOLE AND I'M RUNNING AROUND TRYING TO FIND HER SOMETHING TO EAT. I DON'T UNDERSTAND DREAMS MYSELF...

A WEEK PASSES AND OUR LUCK REMAINS PATHETIC. WE'RE DOWN TO ONE MEAL A DAY. RICE AND COCA COLA. THE MUTTS IN OUR NEIGHBORHOOD BEGIN TO LOOK TASTY. WELL, ALMOST.

I WAKE UP ONE MORNING AND VICENTE'S ALREADY GONE. YOUR CHANCES OF BEING HIRED SOMEWHERE ARE BETTER IF YOU'RE ALONE ANYWAY, SO I GET DRESSED AND I'M OUT THERE.

FUCKING BROAD DAYLIGHT AND[?] THESE KIDS JUMP ME AND STEA[L] MY COAT AND WHAT'S LEFT OF [MY] MONEY.

I SAT THERE BOTH LAUGHING AND CRYING. I SHOULD HAVE SOLD THE COAT MYSELF FOR EXTRA CASH LIKE I HAD PLANNED BEFORE.

FOR A DELIRIOUS MOMENT I THOUGHT OF GOING BACK TO MY WIFE, BUT I CAME TO MY SENSES BEFORE I EVEN SCRAPED MYSELF UP OFF THE DIRT.

I WENT HOME TO GET MY NOT-SO-GOOD COAT AND SET OFF AGAIN. I DIDN'T WANT TO GIV[E] MYSELF ANY TIME TO SIT AROUND THE HOU[SE] TO MOPE IN SELF-PITY.

MIDDAY I WAS FEELING SHITTY; MY SIDES HURT FROM [THO]SE KIDS'GOD DAMN HARD SHOES, I WAS FAMISHED AND [G]ORGEOUS NUBIAN MAIDEN CAUGHT ME PICKING MY NOSE.

I SLIP INTO AN ALLEY TO SPIT UP IN PRIVATE WHEN THIS GUY IN A SHARP SUIT COMES OUT OF THE BACK DOOR OF THIS DINKY RESTAURANT AND HE ASKS ME IF I WANT A JOB. I ALMOST SHIT. IT'S ONLY A LOWLIFE BUS BOY DEAL, BUT THE WAY THINGS ARE GOING...

[I] WALK INTO THE SMALL SMELLY [KITC]HEN AND I MEET THE COOK. I [MAN]AGE TO TALK 'EM INTO A QUICK [MEA]L THAT THEY DEDUCT FROM [MY]PAY. WELL, I TOOK ONE BITE AND [WA]S OUT OF THERE LIKE A FLASH.

I WALKED FAST BECAUSE I DIDN'T WANT TO GIVE MYSELF ENOUGH TIME TO CHANGE MY MIND OUT OF DESPERATION. OR OUT OF SENSE. THE FASTER I WALKED THE MORE ANGRY I GOT. WAS I ANGRY...!

THAT ASSHOLE IN THE SHARP SUIT TELLS ME THAT ANOTHER GUY HAD BEEN IN EARLIER FOR THE JOB BUT THEY DIDN'T HIRE HIM BECAUSE HALF HIS FACE WAS FUCKED UP AND HE MIGHT HAVE KEPT CUSTOMERS AWAY. THEY TOLD HIM IT WAS BECAUSE OF HIS EARRING. AND KNOWING THAT DAMN VICENTE HE PROBABLY BELIEVED 'EM!

[I FO]UND VICENTE AT HOME BUSILY PREPARING A STEAK [DIN]NER FOR THE BOTH OF US. TWO BOTTLES OF COLD GERMAN [BEE]R AWAITED OUR PARCHED PALATES. HIS GOOD SUIT [COA]T WAS NOWHERE TO BE SEEN.

PRIDE. IT'LL KILL YOU, I'M TELLING YOU.

FIM

4

DUCK FEET

BAM
BAM
BAM

GO AWAY! WE MADE A DEAL, REMEMBER? AS LONG AS WE KEEP OUR BUSINESS HERE ON THE EDGE OF TOWN YOU DON'T BUG US, *RIGHT?!*

SHE'S GONE!

WAIT.

SHE'S TRICKY. I'D BETTER CHECK THAT BACK DOOR AGAIN.

WHERE IS HE?

GNNNNAGSHIT--!

WHAT ABOUT OUR DEAL, CHELO?! WE MADE A DEAL!

HE'S GONE AND DONE IT, MEME. ROBERTO'S KILLED HIS GRANDFATHER.

ROBERTO!

YI!

YOU'RE GONNA RUIN MY BUSINESS, DAMN YOU!

THEN TELL ME WHERE YOU'RE HIDING HIM..!

YOU KNOW, MEME, I'M GLAD YOU'RE HIDING HIM. NOW I'LL BE ABLE TO STICK YOUR ROTTEN ASS IN JAIL FOR A COUPLE OF DECADES..!

YOU COPS ARE ALL THE SAME! BULLIES! FASCISTS! YOU'RE NOT HAPPY UNLESS YOU'RE HUMILIATING SOMEONE!

DON'T KILL HER! YOU'RE IN ENOUGH SHIT AS IT IS! JUST GET OUTTA HERE!

SHE DON'T LOOK SO TOUGH TO ME NOW..!

IS IT TRUE, ROBERTO? YOUR GRAMPA..?

GGGGGGGGG...

SFT

THE OLD BASTARD HAD IT COMING! FIRST INTO THEN JOEY THEN ME..BUGGIN' US AND BUGGIN' US AND BUGGIN' US..!

HURRY! AND DON'T FORGET TO SEND US SOMETHING NICE FROM DISNEYLAND!

..DON'T HIT ME! I DIDN'T DO ANYTHING..!

I'LL BE BACK FOR YOUR HIDES LATER...

ROBERTO!

WHAP!

2

EARS AGO AS A
DWIFE CHELO HELPED
ING ROBERTO INTO
E WORLD; NOW AS
ERIFF SHE HAS
ELPED TAKE HIM OUT.
S A SIN, ALL RIGHT. A
OODY SIN..."
SKAR BENEVENTE, 35,
HOE REPAIRMAN

S GRAMPA WAS ALWAYS,
U KNOW, TRYING TO,
...I'M JUST GLAD HE
N'T BUG ME ANYM...
H GOD. THAT'S MEAN,
N'T IT? OH, I'M SO
FUL..."
IANA VILLASEÑOR, 16,
TUDENT

GATO! YOUR BROTHER AND
RANDFATHER AREN'T YET FIVE
NUTES INTO THE GROUND AND
LREADY YOU'RE ACTING SILLY!

WHAT'S DONE
IS DONE, PIPO.
LIFE GOES
ON...

ME AND DEATH HAVE AN
UNDERSTANDING, MI AMOR. I
CALL *HIM* OUT EVERYDAY AND
EVERYDAY *HE* BACKS OFF. I
JUST MAY DECIDE TO LIVE
FOREVER...

OH, DON'T START
WITH YOUR CREEPY
BULLSHIT. CAN'T YOU
SHOW RESPECT FOR AT
LEAST *TEN* MINUTES?
YOU'RE SO COLD...

COLD. ROBERTO KILLED GRAMPA TO **ESCAPE** THE OLD MAN'S DOMESTIC TERRORISM AND SO THE FAMILY HAS THE POOR BASTARDS BURIED NEXT TO ONE ANOTHER; BUT *I'M* COLD..?

OHHH...

SERGIO HONEY, TIME TO GO HOME NOW... *SERGIO?*

TOC TOC TOC TOC TOC

HUFF HUFF HUFF

THERE! WHEW! NOW DON'T RUN AWAY AGAIN, CASIMIRA!

MAMA INNA HOLE!

GUADALUPE...

FOUND HER, MOM! SHE WAS AT THAT FUNERAL READY TO JUMP INTO ONE OF THE OPEN GRAVES.

MAMA..!

WELL, DON'T LET HER FALL IN HERE TOO, GUADALUPE!

TSK, HOPE I DIDN'T BUST MY ARM TOO BAD...YOU'D BET- TER GET CASIMIRA HOME TO OFELIA NOW, LUPE.

THEN CAN I TELL OFELIA TO GET SOME HELP NOW, MOM? *PLEASE?*

NO! I DON'T WANT *ANYBODY* TO KNOW I FELL IN HERE! ...*SO EMBARRASSED...* I'LL FIGURE A WAY OUT MYSELF, HONEY...

GOD, I'M *STARVING* TOO...

TWO.

BUT YOU'RE *HURT!* AND WHO KNOWS WHAT KIND OF GWIGGLY BUGS ARE JUST WAITIN' TO SNEAK INTO THAT CUT IN YOUR ELBOW AND--

JUST TAKE CASIMIRA HOM AND HAVE OFEL MAKE ME SOMETH TO EAT. TELL HE I'M TOO BUSY A THE MOVIE HOU TO LEAVE, OK

IFM.

T,
M...

GO!

GO!

MOM'S THE CRANKIEST PERSON IN THE UNIVERSE WHEN SHE'S HUNGRY, SO IF I DON'T WANT TO SPEND THE REST OF THE MONTH EATING STANDING UP...

SLAM!

OFELIA..!

SHHHHHHH...

BLIB!

OW! IT'S
HMARA, THE
URANDERA.

OFELIA JUST WENT TO SLEEP, CHILD. I HAVE JUST GIVEN HER AN EXHAUSTIVE BACK TREATMENT.

OH, POOR OFELIA. SOMETIMES SHE CRIES CAUSE HER BACK HURTS SO MUCH...

TELL ME, GIRL. I KNOW THE FELLOW IN THE MIDDLE THERE, BUT THE OTHERS..?

FELIA SHLEEB

OH, UM, THAT MAN WAS A HOLLYWOOD MOVIE STAR WHO DIED WHEN DOCTORS TRIED TO FIX HIS BACK..I ALWAYS FORGET HIS NAME...

THE LADY IS FRIDA KAHLO. SHE PAINTED THESE CRAZY LOOKING PICTURES. SHE DIED 'CAUSE HER BACK WAS ALL MESSED UP, TOO. OPHELIA PICKED FRIDA TO BE HER OWN PERSONAL SAINT, WHETHER FRIDA WANTS TO BE A SAINT OR NOT...

I GUESS SHE HAS JESUS UP THERE TOO 'CAUSE IT WAS A CHURCH THAT FELL DOWN ON HER BACK IN THE FIRST PLACE.

SHE'LL SLEEP FOR HOURS. DON'T DISTURB HER.

ZIMM
ZAMM
ZUMM
ZIMM

⑥

NDERA - HEALER, WITCH DOCTOR   ·MOVIE STAR - JEFF CHANDLER

POOR OFELIA. I'VE NEVER SEEN HER SLEEP SO PEACEFUL. I WOULDN'T WAKE HER UP FOR A MILLION DOLLARS.

ZIMM

ZAMM!

ZUMM

ZIMM

BLIVITZ!

HEY, MARICELA! MOM WANTS YOU TO BABYSIT CASIMIRA THIS AFTERNOON -- AND UM, OH, MOM NEEDS SOME MONEY FOR, AH, DINNER TONIGHT...

LEAVE CASIMIRA, B YOU CAN FORGET T DOUGH! LAST TIME YO PULLED THAT ONE YOU W OUT AND BOUGHT YOUR A PARACHUTE!

BUT IT'S THE TRUTH THIS TIME! WHY WOULD I WANT TO LIE AND GET CLOBBERED AGAIN?

FORGET IT, KIDDO. NOW GO, I'M TOO BUSY HERE TO FOOL WITH YOU!

OK, FATSO! IT'S YOUR FUNERAL.

DUMB OL' PARACHUTE HAD HOLES IN IT ANYWAY!

GRUMBLE GRUMBLE

JA-BREW"HAH (WITCH)

TOC TOC TOC TOC

AH, MADAM CONSTABLE. COULD YOU BE SO KIND AS TO DIRECT ME TO WHERE I MIGHT HAVE MY POOR FEET TENDED TO? I'VE COME SUCH A LONG WAY...

C-COME INTO MY OFFICE, SEÑORA. I CAN TAKE CARE OF YOU MYSELF. I WAS ONCE A BAÑADADORA.

OH? YOU ARE VERY GENEROUS, MY DEAR.

...BRUJA! CHELO HAS NOT SEEN ONCE SINCE SHE WAS GIRL. CHELO REMEMBERS HOW SUCH A CREATURE IS DEALT WITH: INDULGE THEM AND HOPE THEY ARE SOON ON THEIR WAY WITHOUT INCIDENT...

GEE, CHELO LOOKED KINDA SCARED. MAYBE WE SHOULDN'T...

SHUT UP! IF CHELO'S GONNA WASH HER FEET, I'M GONNA SEE IF THE BRUJA HAS FLIPPERS OR NOT!

C'MON, DORALIS. WE BETTER GO...

NO! DUCK FEET!

SNORRF...AHHHH, YOU'VE THE HANDS OF AN ARTIST, MY DEAR. I FEEL A PLETHORA OF PREDICTIONS COMING ON... JMMMMMMMM...

C'MON, BOOTS! LET'S FORGET IT! PLEASE..!?

DON'T HAVE DUCK FEET·DON'T HAVE DUCK FEET·JUST BE AN OLD LADY·DON'T HAVE DUCK FEET...

I WANNA SEE--!

JMMM...AMERICAN MOVIEMAKER STEVEN SPIELBERG WINS AN OSCAR FOR HIS ADAPTATION OF *THE CATCHER IN THE RYE* IN 1998. ART THEN IS LEGALLY DECLARED DEAD.

...DADORA / BAÑADORA· BATH GIVER

109

eeeYOWwww!

THE CHILDREN FLEE FOR FEAR OF THE UNKNOWN, SAVE GUADALUPE; SHE RUNS BECAUSE OF WHAT SHE KNOWS...!

...SORRY YOU CAN'T STAY IN OUR TOWN LONGER, SEÑORA...

YES, I MUST BE ON MY--❂

BABY... MY BABY'S GONE...

OUR B--?

THE LEATHER POUCH! MY BABY--!

MAYBE IT'S ON THE FLOOR, OR--

YOU'VE TAKEN IT!

CARCEL

N-NO... I DIDN'T EVEN KNOW YOU-- YOU...UHH...

DEMANDADO

Z

TO BE CON- CLUD- ED IN PART TWO

...BA HAS ACCIDENTALLY FALLEN INTO A [DE]EP PIT AND IS TOO EMBARRASSED TO [GE]T HELP. ONLY HER DAUGHTER GUADALUPE [KN]OWS OF LUBA'S PREDICAMENT BUT THE [CHI]LD WAS SWORN TO SECRECY.

MOM'S LIKE THAT...

AN ALLEGED BRUJA HAS COME TO PALOMAR. A LEATHER POUCH CONTAINING A BABY'S SKULL WAS STOLEN FROM HER BY SOME CURIOUS CHILDREN, BUT DUE TO THEIR CARELESS HORSE-PLAY THE INFANT CRANIUM WAS LOST. THE OLD WOMAN SEARCHES THE TOWN FOR HER "BABY."...

AYYYYYYYYY... DONDE ESTA MI HIIIIIJOOO

✱ WHERE IS MY CHILD? = BRUJA (BREW'HAH) - WITCH

AS IT HAPPENS, THE STOLEN SKULL SITS AT THE BOTTOM OF THE SAME HOLE FROM WHERE LUBA NOW STRUGGLES TO CLIMB OUT...

GUADALUPE? LUPE, HONEY, I CHANGED MY MIND, BABY... GUADALUPE? SON OF A·· LUPE! I WANT OUT SO I CAN KILL WHOEVER CLOBBERED ME WITH THIS··· LUPE!!

OH, YEAH?

TAKE THIS! AND THAT!

PZOW! PZOW!

AS BLOOD GUSHES OUT OF THEIR EYEBALLS THE U.S. SOLDIERS ARE SORRY THEY INVADED OUR TOWN..!

②

SPA FON BAS CROD CHAZ FURND SQUA TRONT

HYAAAH!

DIDN'T THINK I'D SEE THROUGH YOUR DISGUISE, EH, YANKEE TERRORIST SPY?

THOSE ARE *MY* SHORTS YOU GOT ON, ⸮KAFF⸮ TONANTZIN! I THOUGHT SHERIFF CHELO DOESN'T ALLOW GIRLS OVER *18* TO SHOW A LEG ABOVE THE KNEE... ⸮WHEEZ⸮

⸮KAFF⸮

FORGET *CHELO!* SHE'S APPOINTED *ME* SHERIFF SO WHAT *I* SAY GOES!

NOW WHAT THE HELL WERE YOU DOING OUT RUNNING INSTEAD OF BEING HOME IN BED, *DIANA*? YOU GET YOUR MUSCLE BUTT IN BED LIKE *RIGHT NOW!*

OK ⸮COUGH⸮, SISTER DEAR. AND IF I FIND ANY SPYS UNDER MY BED I'LL SEND THEM OVER TO YOU...

HUH. SHE CAN JOKE, BUT NEITHER THE YAN OR THE SOVIETS ARE ABOVE SECRETLY POISON TOWNS SO THAT THEY CAN LATER COME AND OFFER AID TO GET US ON *THEIR* SIDE.

I PUT UP ALL THE SIGNS ON THE OUTSIDE OF TOWN THAT SAY NOT TO COME INTO OUR SICK TOWN LIKE YOU SAID TO DO, SHERIFF CHELO!

OK, MARTÍN. ⸮WHEEZ⸮ AND STOP SHOUTING! GOD...⸮

I BETTER GO TO FIND SHERIFF TONANTZIN AND HELP HER FIND THE BRUJA WHO'S MAKING EVERYBODY SICK I BET!

DEPUTY TONANTZIN... ⸮WHEEZ⸮

THAT'S RIGHT! THROW THE HAG OUT OF TOWN! AT GUN ⸮KAFF⸮ POINT IF YOU HAVE TO! SHE CAN TAKE THIS... *THING* SHE BROUGHT WITH HER ⸮KAF⸮

GODDAMN OLD HAG...*!* GOT ME AND THIS OLD TOWN TURNED ALL UPSIDE DOWN...*BRUJA.* HA! IF I HA THE STRENGTH I'D GO OUT THERE AND... *LISTEN TO ME!* SHE'S JUST AN OLD WOMAN... JUST...

4

OFELIA, WAKE UP! ⸘KAF⸘ YOU SAID IT'S GONNA RAIN-- THAT MEANS THE HOLE MOM'S STUCK IN WILL FILL UP AND-- OFELIA--!

BZAW

FOOEY...THEN I'LL SAVE MOM MYSELF... I'LL SAVE HER AND SHE'LL GET MAD AT EVERYBODY BUT ME AND I'LL BE EATING SWEETS AND ICE CREAM WHILE EVERYBODY ELSE WILL HAVE TO EAT LIVER.

ROMPEL-KNURR

YOU MADE TONANTZIN VILLASEÑOR CHIEF DEPUTY? AND GAVE HER A GUN? CHELO, SHE'S DANGEROUS ENOUGH IN A TIGHT SKIRT...

ACTUALLY, TONANTZIN'S A STRONG, RELIABLE GIRL ⸘KAF⸘ DESPITE THAT DOPEY LOOK ON HER FACE. BESIDES, THE GUN ISN'T LOADED, MIGUEL. SHE INSISTED I GIVE HER ONE. ⸘KAF⸘ I DON'T EXPECT ANY REAL TROUBLE DURING THE COURSE OF THIS...THING.

HUH...ALWAYS THOUGHT YOU DIDN'T LIKE HER. I MEAN, YOU CAME UP WITH THAT GOOFY LEG LAW JUST TO BUG HER...

W YOU LISTEN HERE! I CREATED T LAW TO PRESERVE WHAT WAS T OF THE DIGNITY OF THE WOMEN PALOMAR! MEN COME AROUND AND E TONANTZIN IN HER TINY SKIRT D HER HEELS-- WELL! NO MAN-- BODY RESPECTS A WOMAN WHO OOKS LIKE A TRAMP--A--

W, WELL, L! WHY STOP HERE..?

WHY NOT BURN STENCILED SERIAL NUMBERS ON EVERYONE'S FOREHEAD..?

HEY, AW C'MON, I DIDN'T MEAN IT, I--C'MON, YOU CAN'T GO OUT THERE, NOT IN YOUR CONDITION--CHELO!

⸘COUGH⸘ I'M GOING OUT WHERE THE AIR IS NICE AND MUGGY.

CLANK

HALF OF YOU IS IN THE DARK AGES WHILE THE OTHER HALF IS HERE PROTECTING WHAT YOU LOVE...AND THE WHOLE OF YOU RESTS IN MY HEART.

6

ER, GERALDO, DIDN'T YOU SEE THE WARNING SIGNS OUTSIDE OF TOWN?

DON'T CHANGE THE SUBJECT! YOUR SHERIFF WHAT'S-ER-NAME MURDERED MY COUSIN ROBERTO ALL THE SAME! HE DIED LIKE A COMMON--LIKE A DOG IN THE STREET, LIKE-- HIS HEAD WAS TURNED COMPLETELY BACKWARDS! I WOULDN'T CALL THAT CRIB DEATH...!

YOU FORGET ROBERTO KILLED HIS GRAMPA IN THE FIRST PLACE, GERALDO...

AAAH, YOU KNOW WHAT KIND OF SWINE THE OLD MAN WAS! TREATED EVERYONE LIKE DIRT, LIKE-- HE CAME CLOSE TO MOLESTING YOUR LITTLE SISTER DIANA A FEW TIMES, AS I RECALL...

CHELO DIDN'T MEAN TO KILL YOUR COUSIN. SHE HIT HIM AND HE FELL ...

OH SURE, THAT'S WHAT SHE TOLD EVERYBODY. BUT I'VE BEEN IN AND OUT OF JAIL ALL MY AND I KNOW WHAT SHIT PULL WHEN THEY THINK NO IS LOOKING. COPS. PIMPS POPE. THEY'RE ALL OF THE S BREED. TERRORISTS. KEEP THE PEOPLE IN LINE WITH FEAR...

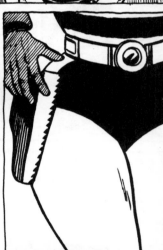

THAT'S CRAZY TALK! MAYBE I OUGHT TO SIT YOU IN A CELL FOR A FEW DAYS TO COOL YOU OFF!

HEH. I AM GOING TO JAIL REAL SOON. BUSTED A BOTTL ACROSS SOME STUPID COP'S FACE AFTER HE POPPED ME FOR COKE. JUMPED BAIL.

THEY'LL FIND ME, NO PROBLEM

AH, BUT ALL THIS SHIT ABOUT COPS AND STUFF IS OLD NEWS. `BUT THAT'S THE WAY IT IS, THE WAY IT'S ALWAYS BEEN, SO FORGET IT' THEY TELL YOU. YEAH, WELL, TELL THAT TO A BLACK KID IN SOUTH AFRICA ...

HEY, WAIT! AREN'T WE STILL GONNA --AW, FORGET IT. GO TO HELL!

GOD, HOW'D A GUY WHO'D BEEN SO GOOD IN THE SACK TURN OUT TO BE SUCH A LOON? CRAZY PEOPLE GIVE ME THE SHIVERS...

MY--MY GUN! GERALDO! DID YOU SEE WHERE I--I--

GERALDO--?

UT WHY WOULD
HE TAKE...

oH SHIT..!

ELO!

CHELO GAVE ME AN EMPTY
GUN 'CAUSE SHE DOESN'T
TRUST ME... *SO I SWITCHED
IT WITH HER LOADED ONE!*

≥SOB≥

I OUGHT TO
KEEP HIM LOCKED
UP FOREVER...
CALLING ME A
NAZI, *HMF.*

I DUNNO...
I ALWAYS TRY TO
DO WHAT I THINK IS
BEST FOR MY
PEOPLE...

MAYBE I NEED
HELP IN RUNNING
THIS TOWN... SOMEONE
STRONG AND *SMART.*
ESPECIALLY SMART.

VOICE
TEXT

AYYYYYYYY
MI
HIIIIIIJoo

*SHOULD HAVE
ONE THIS WHEN I HAD
THE CHANCE...*

OK, LADY!
I THINK IT'S TIME
YOU AND I TALK
AGAIN··❊·

··AYYYYYYYYYY
MII HIIIIIIJO··

!?!

SAY HI TO
OL' GRAMPA FOR
ME, HOG.

ON'T KNOW, SHE'S
NE THERE SOMEWHERE··
! LET ME OUT SO'S
AN HELP FIND HER
O, TON·· HEY!

BOO
HOO

8

119

WHEEZ KAF

WHEEZ KAF

GOTCHA!

YOW

HEY...YOU'RE THE HOLLYWOOD MOVIE STAR WHOSE NAME I ALWAYS FORGET... OFELIA HAS YOUR PICTURE UP IN HER ROOM...

WHEEZ KAF

YOU DIED 'CAUSE YOUR BACK WAS BAD... OFELIA LIKED YOU A LOT A LOT IN THE MOVIES... SOMEDAY SHE'LL DIE 'CAUSE OF HER BAD BACK...

FRIDA!

HEY! IT'S FRIDA KAHLO, THE CRAZY PAINTER! SHE'S SUPPOSED TO BE UP ON OFELIA'S WALL, TOO, 'CAUSE SHE ALSO DIED OF A BAD BACK... I GUESS THEY BOTH COULDN'T STAND OFELIA'S SNORING...

THE ONLY ONE FROM OFELIA'S WALL THAT ISN'T HERE IS JESUS CHRIST, BUT I GUESS HE'S HIDING OUT FROM THE PEOPLE WHO BUG HIM FOR REQUESTS ALL DAY...

OUR JOB IS DONE HERE, MR. CHANDLER.

SHALL WE BE OFF, MRS. RIVERA?

OH, DON'T GO! PLEASE, DON'T GO! PLEASE---OH... I GUESS THEY HAD TO GO BACK TO OFELIA'S WALL TO KEEP JESUS COMPANY...

MOM...

10

121

MOM..MOM, I'M HERE! I MADE IT! I'LL PULL YOU OUT!

CAREFUL YOU DON'T FALL IN, LUPE...

AND..AND OFELIA SAID IT WAS GONNA RAIN AND I THOUGHT YOU WERE GONNA DROWN IN THERE..!

OH, I'M A BETTER SWIMMER THAN THAT, LOVE...

OH, BUT YOU'RE SAFE...YOU'RE HERE...YOU'RE REALLY HERE...

IN THE FLESH, KIDDO

YOU'RE NOT MY MOM!! SHE'S BOO'FUL--WEARS CLOTHES--BOO'FUL--

--A MAN WITH A GOATEE! DID YOU SEE--TSK, OH!! THEN HAVE YOU SEEN SHERIFF CHELO! YOU DO KNOW WHO THAT IS, DON'T YOU? DON'T YOU...OHHH..!

BOO'FULL-- WEARS CLOTHES...

SNIFF SOB BOO HOO... IT'S NO GOOD.. POOR CHELO..SNIFF POOR ME...

MOM...

DO I BELIEVE THERE'S SUCH THING AS BRUJAS?

YOU MEAN BESIDES MY MOM?

OH, MARICELA! WHY ARE YOU SO--KAF? I'M SURE YOUR MOTHER'LL SHOW UP SOMEWHERE.

DROWN... BOOFUL--CLOTHES.. YEAH, UH HUH...GIVE IT BACK, BOOTS! GIVE IT--! DON'T HAVE DUCK FEET! DON'T HAVE DUCK FEET...

SEÑORA SHERIFF CHELO! ♡♡ HI MARICELA ♡♡ LA BRUJA! I SEEN HER IN A TREE!

EATING A BANANA, PROBABLY KAF

JESUS, THIS KID NEEDS HELP BAL WHAT THE HELL KIND OF TOWN IS THIS THEIR KIDS LAY SICK AND NEGLECT IN THE GODDAMN STREET?! BETTER HER TO A DOCTOR BEFORE I D ANYTHING ELSE...!

ZIMM ZAMM ZUMM

CHELO...THAT MAN'S GOT-- GUADALUPE! CHELO, THAT MAN'S GOT MY SISTER!

I SEE HIM..! HEY YOU! HOLD IT RIGHT THERE--!

MOMMM..

WHAT..? HEY, THIS KID'S IN BAD SHAPE! I WAS TAKING HER--

DON'T EVEN MAKE A MOVE! MARICELA, GET YOUR SISTER··

UMILIATE NOW AND ASK QUESTIONS TER, HUH? I'VE HAD COP GUN BARRELS MY ASS BEFORE, COP...SO YOU'RE THE NE WHO DID IT TO ROBERTO...

NOW WE'LL ¿KAFF! GO OVER TO THE KID'S HOME AND ASK HER COUSIN OFELIA ABOUT WHAT'S GOING ON...!

MOVE!

MOVE. IN THE NAME OF THE LAW...

OH...OH, GOD, SHE FOUND HIM OUT BEFORE...OH, THANK GOD...! I OUGHT TO GIVE HIM A PIECE OF MY MIND··!

GUADALUPE, ARE YOU CRAZY?! C'MERE!

MOM!

SO! YOU GOT CAUGHT BEFORE YOU COULD PULL ANY OF YOUR--

ANTZIN!

¡IIIII!

GUADALUPE, DON'T! WHAT'S WITH YOU? GUADALUPE, STOP··

BLEAH...

GO AHEAD, YOU FUCKING MURDERING COW...TELL US ALL HOW YOU REALLY KILLED ROBERTO...GO AHEAD...

I'M GONNA THROW YOU IN THERE IF YOU DON'T STOP··OW!

MA MA MA

12

123

CHELO, ¿SOB¿, CHELO--! HE GOT MY GUN WHEN I WASN'T LOOKING 'CAUSE HE WANTED TO SHOOT YOUR OR SOMETHING AND IT WOULD BE O.K. IF IT WAS THE EMPTY GUN YOU GAVE ME BUT I SWITCHED IT AND NOW IT'S LOADED OH GOD I'M SORRY

ALL RIGHT THEN, STUPID! FALL IN! GO AHEAD!

TONANTZIN... ¿KAF¿ TONANTZIN, I KNEW YOU'D SWITCH GUNS...SO I LEFT BOTH OF THEM EMPTY... THE GUN HE HOLDS ISN'T LOADED!

GUADALUPE..?

WHAT...

AW SHIT--

CLICK CLICK CLICK

WHO THE HELL BEANED ME WITH THIS GODDAMN ¢#·$·*!·?@%!

AAAAA

PRAISE THE HOLY VIRGIN IN HER INFINITE WISDOM GRACE.

EEEEEEEEEEE

THAT'S ENOUGH, TONANTZIN, STOP! STOP..!

ROBERTO DESERVED BETTER-- TO DIE LIKE A MAN... WITH DIGNITY...

SHHHHH, TONANTZIN...IT'S OVER NOW, SHH SHHHH...

TOC TOC

TOC TOC TOC TOC

...ELL, THAT ORDEAL ...ISN'T *ALL* BAD. I ...ST A FEW POUNDS.

IS...YOUR ELBOW ALL BROKEN LIKE YOU THOUGHT?

OH YEAH; NO, JUST CRACKED IT A LITTLE. I GOT OFF EASY COMPARED TO EVERYONE ELSE. COLOMBIA CHACON WENT BLIND FOR A WHILE, BUT SHE'S O.K. NOW. ALMOST ALL OF BOBBY MADRID'S TEETH FELL OUT... AND THAT POOR OLD WOMAN SEARCHING FOR HER -- WELL, WHAT WAS *ONCE* HER BABY...

...REMINDED ME OF OLD ISIDRO ...O LIVES ALONE ON THE BEACH... ...H CRAZY LONESOME BECAUSE ...EONE VERY DEAR TO EACH ...THEM HAS BEEN LOST ...FOREVER...

DON'T KNOW WHAT'D BE WORSE...LOSING SOMEONE WHERE I COULD NEVER BE WITH THEM AGAIN...

OR HAVING THAT SOMEONE ALWAYS CLOSE BY BUT HAVING LOST THEM JUST THE SAME...

I'LL NEVER LOSE *YOU* 'CAUSE I'M NEVER LETTING YOU GO *EVER EVER EVER*...!

OOFG -- WITH THAT GRIP, I BELIEVE IT..!

TONANTZIN...

I'M NOT CHANGING, SHERIFF! I CAN WEAR ANYTHING I WANT...

OH, TONANTZIN...I JUST WANTED TO KNOW HOW YOU WERE, HONEY...

AS WELL AS A PERSON CAN BE WHILE A MILLION BOMBS SIT READY TO BE DROPPED ON OUR HEADS. THE THREAT OF BEING BOMBED AT ANY GIVEN MOMENT MAKES FOR A BETTER PRISON THAN ANY BARS EVER DID.

WHAT WITH LIBYA AND THE U.S. AND THE U.S.S.R. AND--WELL, WHEN YOU HAVE MISSILE SILOS HIDDEN UNDER SCHOOLS AND SHIT-- AND SHIT! THE U.S. ARE NOW PREPARING BOMBS THAT'LL HAVE ALMOST WORSE EFFECTS THAN THEIR MOST POPULAR BOOKS AND MOVIES.

GERALDO'S GOT IT FIGURED OU SO WE'RE GONNA WRITE TO EACH OTHER AS THINGS PROGRESS...OR DETERIORATE, IF YOU WILL...

I CAN WEAR ANYTHING I WANT, SHERIFF!

I DON'T KNOW...TONANTZIN'S ALWAYS BEEN A BIT GOOFY, BUT NOT-- FIRST TIME SHE DIDN'T ADDRESS ME BY MY NAME... ·ULP·

TONANTZIN GETTING WEIRD? HUH! ANY KIND OF MOVEMENT IN MY SISTER'S BRAIN COULD ONLY BE AN IMPROVEMENT. OH, I WOULDN'T WORRY, CHELO. SHE'LL BE ALL RIGHT...

OK, DIANA... I JUST THOUGHT MAYBE THAT ORDEAL WITH ROBERTO'S COUSIN HAD--WELL...OK...

...OR HAVING THAT SOMEONE ALWAYS CLOSE BY BUT HAVING LOST THEM JUST THE SAME...